INTO THE MIST

INTO THE MIST

When Someone You Love Has
Alzheimers Disease

Deborah Uetz with
Dr. Anne Lindsay

To order additional copies of this book, contact:
Xlibris Corporation
1-888-795-4274
www.Xlibris.com
Orders@Xlibris.com
28424

CONTENTS

OUR JOURNEYS THROUGH THE MIST:
FRANK, SHIRLEY, AND JACK

THROUGH THE LOOKING GLASS

A MAP THROUGH THE MIST: HELPING YOU COPE

ESSENTIAL INFORMATION
FOR NAVIGATING THE MIST

This book is dedicated to the men and women who find themselves lost in the fog of Alzheimer's disease. Their struggle and courage is acknowledged and honored. Most especially this book honors Frank, Jack and Shirley whose stories will inform and inspire others.

Also dedicated to the memory of my brother Keith who gave all that he had for dad.

6/17/1953-12/22/2002

Thank you to Renee Reeves "Ask Dutchy" for providing a support forum for families struggling with the challenges of caring for those with Alzheimer's disease. *www.mycarelink.net*

Introduction

by Deborah Uetz

This book is going to take you on a journey. It takes you along as three Alzheimer's patients and their families' deal with the early, middle and final stages of the disease. Their stories are told by their daughters. Along with these personal accounts you will learn coping strategies and resource information.

Jack, Frank and Shirley were healthy members of the world community when Alzheimer's became a part of their lives. Rose, Laurie and I are the daughters of those three people and just as their fates were much the same; our lives too became similarly affected.

The objective of this book is to assist your family as your loved one begins to walk the path which no one would take by choice. It is my desire that you will be better equipped to assist them after having read this book. It is a course with many obstacles but with the benefit of our hindsight and the factual information within these pages perhaps your families passageway will be made less treacherous.

Rose and I became friends when we began to search for information about Alzheimer's disease. She lived half a world away in Australia, but the commonalities of our day-to-day lives were astounding. As we exchanged conversation it became evident that our fathers were at similar points in their illnesses.

Laurie's mother's struggle with Alzheimer's was one of only a few of those I personally encountered who had developed symptoms early in life. Most of the caregivers I met were caring for late onset Alzheimer's patients. I knew that Laurie's mother's story was an important part of this book.

Once you have read the stories of Frank, Jack and Shirley you may find yourself thinking that we compared notes and wrote about experiences that were similar. Actually I was surprised by the similarities. Some of the things mentioned are almost identical in nature and that is one of the amazing aspects of this disease.

The title of this book refers to the way dementia comes upon a loved one, almost imperceptible, undetectable except in hindsight. The mist thickens and surrounds them and you are caught up in the fog as well. With each step you take you can see a bit further, but only a bit. The mist doesn't lift and give you a clear vision of what is ahead. When it has vanished your loved one is gone and you are startled by the clearness of the horizon. You have lived in the mist for so long that it seemed a normal atmosphere. Its absence will seem surreal.

As you will learn in this book there are some things about Alzheimer's and other forms of dementia that one can expect, but never predict. If it were possible I would tell you how to move your loved one through each stage without hitting those obstacles. If the answers were available I would share them with you. Unfortunately, there is no "right way" to give care. There are many things you can do to make the Alzheimer's patient feel more secure. I hope you will find the book very useful as you read personal accounts as well as professional recommendations and scientific information.

Many first time parents arm themselves with child development books and expect their child to hit each milestone at the prescribed time. Only experience will teach them that a child will sit up when it is ready and walk when it is ready, regardless what the books may say. Information won't hasten a baby's development and a book won't provide you with every answer. Similarly this book will help guide you, but realize that your loved one's passage will not follow any roadmap precisely. If our combined experiences help you, even one day of your life then it was worth writing this book.

Dr. Anne Lindsay's extensive experience as a neuropsychologist will provide you with a clinical base of information in order that you may better understand the psychological ramifications for the patient as well as the care provider. She will shed new light on the emotional roller coaster that the Alzheimer's patient and their family will encounter.

This book is primarily for the family or caregiver of a person with dementia. During the time that my father had Alzheimer's disease I read everything that I could find about the disease. It would be presumptuous for me to try to tell you what it is like to have Alzheimer's. I hope that I never have that experience; however, at the end of the book I will list resources that are written by Alzheimer's patients. If you yourself are an Alzheimer's patient, please read their stories. You will find a kinship, I am sure. Also included in the book are poems written by Frank during his illness. His beautiful prose gives us unique insight.

It is such a source of comfort when someone who has been a caregiver connects with another caregiver and discovers that the actions they found so unusual were actually rather universal. That isn't to say that every Alzheimer patient behaves the same way. They are as distinctive as they were before the disease; however, there are common situations that most caregivers encounter.

This will be an emotionally challenging book for you. If your loved one is in the early stages it will be difficult to learn what the future may hold as their disease progresses. You will know when the time comes that you must put the book down, take a deep breath and proceed. Knowledge is power, and understanding of the nature of this illness will better prepare you for the coming days, months and perhaps years. I have chosen to tell you the stories of Jack (my father), Frank and Shirley at the beginning of the book. Reading their stories will be hard but it will also be of the most benefit to you as you try to cope with the care giving role.

When I began the book, Dad was about to be diagnosed. When I finished, my father had already passed away. Every time I hear of another person diagnosed with Alzheimer's disease, I remember that feeling of being overwhelmed with questions. Hopefully this book will answer many of those questions for you. My father and Frank moved through the stages quickly, more quickly than most. Keep in mind that many Alzheimer's patients live many years with the disease.

Anne R. Lindsay, Ph.D.

The first time I heard the term "Alzheimer's disease" it was being applied to my beloved grandmother. It was about 1968, few people had heard of Alzheimer's disease, and many of her grandchildren had trouble even remembering the name of this disease that crept stealth-like into our lives. Although Alois Alzheimer first wrote in 1906 about what came to be known as Alzheimer's disease, the wealth of information we have today about Alzheimer's was absent when my grandmother was diagnosed. The now well-known Alzheimer's Association didn't come into being until nine years after my grandmother's death.

"Nanny," was a proud, dignified gentlewoman who always carried her Richmond, Virginia heritage with her. Her white gloves shone spotless in the sunshine, her gardens reflected talents that were noted in her position as President of the Garden Club of America, she was the epitome of a southern gentlewoman. But Nanny never hesitated to sit on the floor and play "War" or "Spit in the Ocean" with her grandchildren or stand laughing as she watched our grandfather "Poppop" whiz us around their lawns in their old, weathered wheelbarrow. The dress-up trunk she kept for us was rivaled by none, at least in the mind of her adoring granddaughter. And she was a courageous rogue: she championed environmental causes long before it was the fashion and she delighted in working in my father's, her son-in-law's, political campaigns and later participated with wholehearted enthusiasm in New York City events when he was Mayor of New York. This was the magnificent woman who slowly disappeared as Alzheimer's took over her once indomitable mind and spirit.

Early on, Nanny knew there was something horribly wrong and she was frightened. Through diagnosis and afterward I don't know how much any of us grasped the implications of the early problems she was experiencing or the diagnosis. I know I didn't. I did grasp what came later, though. Nanny slowly slipped away until she didn't recognize any of us and she was virtually unrecognizable. Her dignity sapped, she seemed to be in her own prison, one that was confusing and heartbreaking to a loving granddaughter. My grandfather managed to keep her at home with round-the-clock nursing, something few families can manage with the often exorbitant costs of caring for a person with Alzheimer's today.

Nanny died in 1971 and she is still missed. Fortunately, long afterward, I don't remember the Nanny that Alzheimer's stole. I remember sitting in her lap and spinning a favorite charm on her charm bracelet. I remember the special trips I took on the train to see her and revel in her spoiling and loving her grandchildren. I remember her patient, loving exasperation with the "styles" her grandchildren sported during the 1960s and her attempts to take us on shopping sprees to entice us to exchange ripped jeans and peasant blouses for dresses that fell to ladylike knee lengths. I remember the woman who knew us and loved us. My brain has, mercifully, let me forget the years that she was entrapped by Alzheimer's.

I was in graduate school many years later when my mother told me over the phone that Dad had been diagnosed with Parkinson's disease. Guilt immediately set in—I wasn't aware that he had been having new problems that warranted seeing a neurologist. He had been beset by health problems in the past— two heart surgeries, an intestinal blockage requiring emergency surgery, two strokes, and a hemorrhage that took the vision from his one good eye (he was legally blind in the other) had taken some toll, although you never would have known it by Dad's attitude and fortitude. And the same was true throughout the years that Parkinson's became part of our lives. His courage was remarkable. I know there were brief moments when he thought "why me," but they were quickly banished. My mother's attitude had much to do with his ability to not only endure but, to the extent possible, thrive for so many years. She undertook everything that had to be done matter-of-factly, as she has everything else in her life. She would talk about some of the struggles she had, but in my experience it was only with prodding. She, too, rarely complained.

Like so many family members these days, I had to live part of that time frustratingly far away, a half a country to be exact, from my family of origin. Dad's voice became increasingly weak and difficult to understand when we talked over the phone and, as I feared would happen, one of the falls he was beginning to take resulted in a broken hip. My mother often sounded exhausted when I talked to her. Parkinson's was taking its toll.

Mom and Dad finally moved to a retirement community in South Carolina. It was a blessing. Mom reached out for much needed help and was able to hire wonderful women who worked for the retirement community and who came to take care of Dad daily. It was the first time in years Mom was able to take any time for herself; she had become as much a prisoner of Parkinson's as had Dad. But there were still many long nights when she had to forgo sleep to care for Dad.

Dad didn't complain. He never lost his impish sense of humor and to the end he kept abreast of intricate political events. He beamed when he saw his children and particularly his grandchildren. He delighted in the wonderful women who cared for him in South Carolina and they in him. There were cognitive changes that one sees with Parkinson's disease, many of which only I saw due to my background and some that were more obvious. Often we could tell that he was acutely aware of everything around him but couldn't communicate his thoughts.

Dad died last December. It was from pneumonia, as is so often the case with Parkinson's, Alzheimer's, and so many other degenerative conditions. As difficult as it was, I felt that he had been set free. Always healthy and athletic before Parkinson's became too advanced for even Dad to battle, I pictured him sprinting around heaven, donning a pair of skis and shushing down cloud after cloud, getting up a game of doubles tennis with his sister

Jane and brothers Dave and George, and talking to them without hesitation or difficulty. I pictured him free.

And, in March 2004, Mom died. She was diagnosed with advanced ovarian cancer two years before her death. Her first surgery in New York was just the first salvo in the battle, one that she fought with amazing grace and courage. She later developed complications that required massive surgery, after which I spent two months caring for her at her house in South Carolina. She did pretty well until the cancer finally advanced too far and won. When it was clear that nothing more could be done, we spent a month at her house in South Carolina, a month in which we made end-of-life decisions. Ever the realist, Mom prepared living wills and had all of her other affairs in order decades ago, so those weren't issues. But we had to decide where Mom wanted to die, among other issues. We then spent another month at my sister's house in Florida, with Mom surrounded by family and cared for both by family and wonderful hospice professionals. And this I want you to remember: those times are some of the ones I cherish the most of many wonderful moments throughout my relationship with my mother. There were funny moments, tender ones, and we developed a closeness that left me with a sense of peace and happiness when she died, and does to this day. As much as I wish Mom was still here and cancer had never entered our lives, I will also forever love the moments we spent together, from her first surgery to curling up with her in bed and holding her while she slipped away and died. Death is inevitable, and it is within our power to embrace the process and let our love show us the way, or to turn our backs on it and make it a horrifically frightening, noxious process.

As family members we have unique reactions to someone we love being diagnosed with and then living with degenerative conditions. In the remarkable book that follows, three daughters have shared their stories and that of their parents as they were diagnosed and lived with Alzheimer's disease.

The stories are unique but the experiences are shared. As we navigate this territory that has become all too familiar to families worldwide and share our experiences, we learn and help each other to tread perhaps less clumsily, with more confidence, with humor and shared tears, and with the knowledge that we are not alone.

So many years ago, no one could have prepared us for what Nanny went though—few really knew. Thanks to the generosity and eloquence of the three women here and their families, those who read this book will know they're not alone, they'll find invaluable information to help with the practical aspects of being family members and caregivers for someone with Alzheimer's disease, and you'll find that spark of recognition that allows for a relieving sigh when you know that help is out there and your path can be traveled hand-in-hand with others that walk the path with you.

Authors note: To avoid the awkward use of avoiding gender bias by the use of "he/she" or "him/her," we have opted to use the practice of referring to only one gender at a time and have tried to alternate between masculine and feminine and to avoid gender bias.

Alzheimer's is a specter, a piece of mist that holds Dad, me and my family in place with invisible strings. They bind our hearts, our souls and our lives. A never-ending misery from which only death can release us.

Rose Steele

Our Journeys Through the Mist:

Frank, Shirley, and Jack

FRANK

Cup's Empty

by Rose Steele

Imagine . . . .

Imagine you didn't know . . . its just not there, the thought, the word, the idea, the ability, the knowledge . . . the . . . .

Have you ever wanted to make a statement or finish a sentence using a particular word—you know the word and you jokingly say, "it's on the tip of my tongue," and laugh but the irritation of not being able to recall it just then just about drives you nuts? Finally when the word comes, you feel that overwhelming relief and laugh some more. Have you ever gone shopping all morning and when you get home tired, you've at least had the sense of something accomplished? Ever gone to do something, something you do everyday, having a "blank" and said to yourself, "I know this," and then made yourself sit down and start your thought processes anew? Thirty seconds later suddenly the knowledge pops into your head and you continue your task without giving it another thought.

Now imagine someone who never recalls the word, doesn't remember shopping all morning, never has the light bulb moment of knowledge. Imagine the sense of frustration, anger or helplessness that would entail.

Imagine these things happening to you and when you regain your sense of the present becoming upset that "something is wrong," "something is the matter with me."

We learned in retrospect, looking back from the middle or final stages of Dad's illness to the time frame that we deemed would have been "onset" to see what was going wrong.

I can remember a feeling of something wrong when I was in my twenties, a perception that Dad was worried unnecessarily about things, that he was more inclined to get snakey at something that wouldn't have ordinarily bothered him. But he had retired, was working long hours on his story and poetry writing as well as doing the normal running repairs to the house and property. He still painted beautifully. I actually remember at one point saying to Mum when he had forgotten something for the umpteenth time that, "Maybe he has Alzheimer's," and Mum's reply of, "He's just tired."

At that stage I had no knowledge of Alzheimer's at all. It was just something you said in jest. I say it myself even now when I have forgotten something. "Oh, you know, it's just the Alzheimer's kicking in."

In those years one thing I did find peculiar but never said so was Dad making me promise time and again that we would never put him into an institution when he grew old. I promised each time but never understood why. I found out much later that he had made Mum promise the same thing. He knew something was wrong and didn't want to end up in "the nut house." The fact that he had that knowledge became painfully obvious later on. Which begs the question, "why didn't he go to a doctor?" My best guess would be that he was frightened he was going insane.

The years drifted by. For the most part he was his normal self with occasional changes in temperament or personality, which were normally put down to him being tired or cranky or both. When the storm finally broke, we were unprepared.

The first stage of Alzheimer's I found I was largely unaware and by the end stages, you have learned to deal with and to accept the things that happen every day and even hope for peace. The middle stages of Alzheimer's were the longest. It went for years and in that time was when everything seemed to happen.

I remember taking him to one of those assessment things where he was unable to recall the day, date, month, or year. I could see he was still trying to cover not knowing by looking the doctor directly in the eye to bluff his way through. To his credit the doctor didn't even smile when in answer to his question, "how old are you now?" Dad's straight-faced answer was "247. I'm going to live til I'm 100 and then start on my next hundred."

Things happen in slow motion. There is always a time when you can't see the wood for the trees. Alzheimer's is like that. When changes happen they are so imperceptible that they cause only minor irritation and are easily forgiven and forgotten. Then you become aware of what is really going on around you and you think, "I'm sick of this, you have been doing *that* for a little while and it irritates me. Why are you doing that—you never have before."

The big change in Dad was trust. He trusted people less and looked behind every word to see if you were trying to get the better of him. He started to put everything away. Tools from down the shed were eventually moved into the house under the pretext that they were his "good" tools and didn't want them left downstairs. He had a room used solely for him to write or paint in and as time progressed, he started to hide more and more things in his room, which became off limits to everybody. He was noticeably uncomfortable when someone was in the room with him. I often wondered whether the way things were in the Depression here in Australia played a role in how things were hoarded and hidden by Dad. Hiding things became a way of life. He would wrap things in paper or rags and disappear. When he came back he wouldn't have them and could never remember where they were. Bankbooks, money, glasses, and false teeth all went the same way. I now know it is a part of the disease. When things became lost, someone was immediately to blame—they had stolen them.

Another change was disorientation. He would wake up in the morning and ask, "Who am I," "Where are we?" "How did I get here?" and "What's this place?" and Mum would have to explain it all sometimes by going back as far as his childhood. This eventually turned into wanting to go home, something he would tell you daily or several times a day. It's no good trying to explain to someone with AD that they are at home. They don't believe you and the question comes out again 30 seconds later. Better to try and redirect them somehow. Catastrophic reactions in your loved one are frustrating, angering, upsetting, and completely unavoidable. You can do things to evade them sometimes but definitely not always.

By 1997, he was mixing up the names of things like pencils and pens until they were all pencils. Shirts became coats, and he had trouble differing between inside and outside. Topics of discussion were invariably about Ipswich and Woody Point, places of his childhood and his twenties and thirties. He spoke a lot about school, about the bullies in the schoolyard, run-ins with teachers and what he did about them (Dad was always the conquering hero).

Revisiting World War Two was the least favorite and the most widely discussed subject. It started out as recalling things but as time progressed there were a few times (not many) where there was an inability to differentiate between then and now. He went through a worrying period of saying he was going to kill someone and the subsequent sharpening of a steel spear to protect himself. The spear was near the side of the bed, and Mum was sure a sharp tomahawk was in his room. We decided that they, Mum and Dad, would need to go shopping or to the library and I would go on "search and destroy" missions in their house. Over the period of about two weeks, I went into the house and removed the spear, several pieces of sharpened wood, a metal ruler sharpened across the end, a tomahawk, a machete, and half a dozen cut throat razors. They were all sharpened beautifully. He never missed them and probably wouldn't remember where they were. They were well hidden but we felt better they were no longer on the property.

Leaving taps on and walking away, unable to do up shoelaces and buttons, cutting his fingernails with secateurs, lathering up his face to shave with Deep Heat Menthol Rub (ouch), and using his toothbrush to shave with were common. He used the nailbrush from the bathroom to clean his shoes and for shoe polish used artist's paints in Cadmium Red and Vandyke brown. Things not his own started to disappear—6 brand new pairs of Mums knickers, face washers from the linen cupboard went into his desk shelves and running "discussions" happened when he was not allowed to take things he thought were his. He would get upset and it would cause catastrophic reaction so we would let him take them, spy on the hiding place if we were quick and simply un-hide the object again. Clothes removed at the end of the day found their way back into the wardrobe with the clean things. He became confused about the time of day. He would be more agitated in the late afternoon and angry if Mum refused to come to bed at the same time of night, anywhere from six p.m. to ten p.m. Getting up at two a.m. to get dressed and start the day was a habit that, once started, didn't disappear until well into his last months. When feeling vulnerable he would tell us that he is still as good as he ever was and was going to outlive everyone. The oft repeated saying was that he was going to live until he was 100 and then start on his second hundred.

We had some hilarious moments, some laughing with Dad but definitely some brought on by his actions and reactions to what was going on around him. He was a bit of a larrikin (rascal) and when the council did the concrete driveway down the footpath outside their house, Dad pressed a coin into the wet cement to have a giggle at people trying to pick it up as they walked by. Unfortunately it backfired and months later, he tried several times himself to remove it. When it came to the crunch and Dad had to have access to the toilet when he wanted it, it was not unusual for someone to have to jump off and vacate the room for him. Dad walked with shuffling steps and you could hear him coming a mile off. To really "get" someone, you had to shuffle across the bathroom tiles to the toilet door and wriggle the door handle. The occupant would yell "Hang on Dad" and get out in record time only to lose the seat to the more unscrupulous person with the wide smile. The same thing worked wonderfully well for the shower. Once when one of the kids was resting an elbow on the card table he used, he yelled "NO NO NO NO NO" When she asked "What?," he stuck his tongue in and out and waved his hands around—but he was deadly serious. She had to politely leave the room to laugh.

On Mum's birthday and at Christmas, I would buy a small gift and tell Dad he asked me to buy it for him. Dad was pleased to be reminded and to have a gift for her. It would take an hour to wrap and another half an hour to write something because you would have to show him how to draw letters. He always wanted to write, "To Val, Happy Birthday," and then sign his name. He would always smile sweetly and thank me for reminding him and say "I'll never forget this, which of course he would two minutes later. It's still a nice memory.

Security becomes of paramount importance during the middle stages. Still agile enough to walk but without the mental facility to find your way is a bad combination. They can just decide to "go home" and walk out. After a heart-stopping search around the neighborhood a few times, you tend to get very, very careful. You live in a locked atmosphere and are constantly on your guard when your loved one is out in the yard. You must try to give the person with Alzheimer's some independence without knowing that you are watching them like a hawk. During this stage when we were so tired from not sleeping well and having to deal with endless questions, we would point blank refuse to open the security door (the keys to everything was worn around Mum's neck, always). Dad would stand at the door and rattle it and at one stage stood screaming "HELP" until the neighbors came over. Mum explained that Dad had Alzheimer's and that everything was okay but you still wonder what they were thinking as they walked away. To avoid a bad reaction once, we unlocked the door and he promptly and angrily walked out of the gate and up the street being trailed by yours truly. Thankfully he had to rest and sat at a bus stop. My son driving by on his way home stopped to see what the matter was and offered Dad a lift home. It was graciously accepted; Ben drove Dad back up the street and was thanked politely for the lift. Dad was happy to see Mum and went straight inside with her. I walked back up the street with the little black cloud over my head not knowing that Dad's personality had done a complete flip in the one minute car ride home.

Once we had bought our property, Dad and Mum were coming to live with us so we could help care for Dad as he needed more help and so that Mum would not have to cope alone. It took days to clean and pack his room. We found most of his poetry very carefully hidden among painting blocks, shoved into backs of drawers, under the table behind all manner of tools, baskets and boards put up especially to conceal them. Most things in his room were pulled apart and made unusable, including office supplies. We found vast quantities of A4 paper hidden everywhere. Drill bits, small files, rasps, pulled apart pens, string, rubber bands, boxes and boxes of staples, little pieces of paper an inch or so square all were carefully hidden. The biggest surprise was finding his false teeth, lost for three years.

The most touching was the proof that all those years he knew something was wrong. We found hand written instructions to himself. On the inside cover of a book the note, "Start reading here." On another, "Write from this page." Dad used to be able to easily and quickly add a column of four-digit figures. I've seen him do it. We found scraps of paper with simple sums like: $197+197+84=478$, with a tick for being correct. Even when the sum he had written was wrong when totaled, he had given himself a tick. Sometimes there were no ticks, just the working out. Cleaning out his shed, we found mowers and weed eaters completely dismantled and parts hidden everywhere. Most things had to be thrown away because we just couldn't find the pieces.

When things became too much and Dad wanted to "get away from here," I would get phone call after phone call and, to placate him (because I didn't know what else to do), we would tell him he could come to live on the farm. This went on for a couple of years while we were up north because I knew as soon as he got off the phone he wouldn't recall the conversation. It helped when the move was actually on. Mum would tell him they were going to move to the farm and I think it helped because of the history of conversations. We were careful to leave the big furniture where it was and remove the packed boxes to a storage facility so his environment didn't change drastically. He was upset the actual day but I think it was handled as well as possible. Wanting to go home became more intense for a while. Dad and Mum stayed in the main bedroom and had an ensuite to themselves and settled in well. Once the attached granny flat was finished the move across was done quickly with, it seems, no adverse reaction.

I don't agree with children being protected from the effects of Alzheimer's disease. I think they are very aware of what is going on around them. How they handle it is as individual as how we do, and possibly more so because they take their cue from adults around them. We have five children aged nineteen, eighteen, sixteen, sixteen, and fifteen, and they have grown up over the last five years in close proximity to Dad and his deteriorating health. They have all reacted differently; I found the two older kids didn't cope with things as well as the three younger ones. Whether the difference was age or the change in Dad's personality and the granddad they knew previously or just personal likes and dislikes, I don't know. The older two, Ben and Elysha, would help out when needed to but generally felt uncomfortable and made themselves scarce when they could. Going through their own upheavals probably didn't help. The three younger girls coped remarkably well and in different ways. The twins were absolute chalk and cheese. Holly, more shy, would not do things like taking a naked granddad back to get dressed and would generally pass this job to her twin Kate. However she would patiently sit and feed granddad or try to get him to drink, take him walking in the wheelchair, and attempt to engage him in conversation (usually she would speak and hope for an answer). Kate would be all hands on deck and nothing at all phased her. She would help re-dress, feed, change soiled clothes, clean up and sometimes toss poor grandma out of the granny flat with stern words not to come back until she has had at least 30 minutes break. Remarkably our youngest, Tamara, was the one that found a lot of common ground with Dad. She would sit and get him to color in or do some other activity that drove Mum and I round the twist.

Having asked them what affected them the most, their reply was how it affected our immediate family unit. Not going out or on holidays was probably the biggest drawback. Having friends at school ask what they did on the weekend and having to say they did nothing but watch a bit of television. Trying to organize a family day out that never came off because other family members couldn't "baby-sit" for one reason or another happened quite often.

Getting out was great, but they felt guilty that I couldn't go too. The kids also said they have a lot of funny memories about granddad and the things he used to do. Describing the faces he used to pull at them and how he reacted to their amusing themselves at his expense had them laughing so hard they nearly fell off their chairs. He would tell them how he was going to eat them or, if they sat too close to the television, it would blow up and scar their faces. He would want to go to bed and take their hands to go down the hall banging them accidentally into the wall on the way. When he got into bed, they would have to lie down too and then he would get up immediately and go outside. Once watching a show called Rage, a top 40 music clip show, he saw a group singing and dancing and he started to yell, "Who are all these people?" and tell them to get out of the house. The kids would turn off the set and he would say, "thank God they're gone."

To the question, "Are you sorry we kept granddad at home to look after him?," the answer was an emphatic "No!" To, "Are you upset about the things you may have missed out on compared to other kids your age?" they said "Get real Mum, we can go on holidays and other stuff now." Out of the mouths of babes.

> Dear Dad,
>
> I want to write you a letter. I love you but I'm glad you're dead. Lots of love, Rose xxxxx
>
> Now anyone reading that should not take it at face value.

Let me tell you about my Dad. Years before this mongrel disease took hold, Dad lived to chase wild brumbies and wilder mountain creek cattle in the bush and mountains around the Goodna area in Queensland, Australia. He did a stint at timber felling and worked at a large cattle station up in the Northern Territory. He attended bush dances and reportedly cut a pretty good rug.

When World War II broke out, Dad joined the army and fought at Milne Bay, New Guinea. We often asked him as children, how did he survive the war and the answer was always the same: I could run faster than the Japs' bullets. We always believed him of course. To make an extra quid, he and his mates would stand in the brothel lines and when they reached the top of the line would sell their place to the Yanks and then go stand at the bottom of the line again.

After demobilization, he turned his hand to baking and eventually fathered thirteen children. Dad worked two or three jobs at a time to provide for his family. He added rooms to homes, built stockyards and animal shelters, planted fruit and vegetable gardens, looked after goats and slaughtered them for meat. He whistled always. He took inconsolable babies and hoisted them up over his shoulder where they would "miraculously" fall asleep within minutes. He took the time to teach me the fine art of using a crosscut saw, how to change a fuse or how to track something because "girls should know how to as well." You didn't push him too far or you would end up weeding endless gardens to atone for your sins. His favorite line was "cups empty" and you would be banished to the kitchen to make the hundredth cup of coffee that day. He was always very close to Mum, two halves of the same whole. For her he wrote:

TO VAL, MY WIFE © *F.J.Burnham*

> When day dawns no more
> And there is only night,
> As cold and lonely
> As a curlew's cry;
> I will search and strive
> With all my might,
> Until it is at your side
> That I stand, steadfast, by.

All fairly normal you'd say. We don't know when we really noticed the changes in him and even now we think "do you remember when . . ." and then wonder if that was the start. Changes were very slow and he was still his normal self in-between. Over the ensuing years the major change in him was that he trusted no one. He would look out the corners of his eyes without moving his head when someone came into the room, he would put tools away in his room "so some bastard won't steal it," would call the police, he lost things (false teeth, glasses, money), he would tell us he's still the man he used to be and wouldn't back down if it came to using his fists, he didn't want to leave the house. We would put these things down to him being tired or getting old and cranky. The light bulb moment came for Mum when they were putting a simple catch on a door for Grandma. Dad simply did not know how to do it and Mum had to coach him all the way to get the job done. A frightening car ride with Dad at the wheel clinched it. He was diagnosed as probably having Alzheimer's disease in 1992.

I would get regular phone calls from Dad asking me to come and get him because "he can't take this anymore and had to get away." What from, we never knew. Mum suffered the worst when he was unable to recognize who she was, or worse, that she was his mother (Grandma was not the nicest of people from what we can gather and he had not had a wonderful childhood). As the anxiety and confusion mounted for Dad, both Mum and Dad were dealing with the decline in health of Mum's mother, who was living next door. This added more confusion for Dad because he believed that Mum was *always* over next door. Dad wrote this when he was in hospital:

AND I—AM ALL ALONE © F.J. Burnham

My world is turning in the dark
I feel the chill of flesh and bone
I hear music sounding—from the park?
My world is cold—and I—am all alone.
I hear footsteps on my treads that creak,
And in my chest there rests a stone.
My world is turning in the dark
My world is cold—and I—am all alone.
All around me is dark and bleak.

I feel so helpless on my own.
I hear footsteps on my treads that creak.
My world is cold—and I—am all alone.
I feel afraid, so helpless—meek.
Oh God, how can I atone?
All around is dark and bleak.
My world is cold—and I—am all alone.

For any family dealing with this disease, you make decisions regarding what to do and how to handle the welfare of your loved one. To some it means having to make the extremely hard decision of putting their loved one into a nursing home. For Mum it was that she would nurse him at home. For my husband Ron and I and our five kids it was pulling up stakes and moving lock stock and barrel from North Queensland back to Brisbane to help.

Alzheimer's disease impacts your life so completely. It affects your emotional connection to the person with Alzheimer's, spouses and children and family in general and also your financial position. For Mum: the dream of traveling around Australia in retirement, recovering from bringing up all those kids and working endless hours by just painting, writing poetry and relaxing in each others company to laughingly argue whether the word is either or *either*, or neither or *neither*. The reality was quite different. Answering endlessly repetitive questions, getting up in the middle of the night to see what Dad is up doing at two a.m., living in a locked environment to foil any escapes, cleaning up when the bath is mistaken for a urinal, trying to find something for your loved one to do—that he *can* do, never being able to relax for one minute.

We bought and moved onto a property and because of the level of care needed, Dad and Mum moved out with us. As the disease progressed Dad started to fall so we walked everywhere with him, he stopped eating (no thank you, I've eaten) so we would put enough on a plate for a 6 month old which he may or may not touch. No activity would rouse his interest so we took to putting books of horses in front of him which he would try to rip up. It's sad to see this happen to someone who was so full of life.

There were also times when something happened to cheer us up. He had become frightened of horses but it made us smile when, having wheelchaired him downstairs and up to the fence, Sally, a 16HH stock horse put her head towards Dad over the fence and he stretched up to touch her muzzle. I wish I had had a camera with me. At times in the middle of a bad day, he would become calm and give Mum that smile like they knew something we didn't. The look on his face when looking at a grandchild (we knew he still had it . . . somewhere).

The last two years of Dad's life were dotted with various "stages" as we called them. The saddest was "reliving the war stage," which I wished we could have erased from his memory banks to save him pain and anxiety. The worst being "not nice." He would twist fingers, hit and kick. In his defense, it was because we were doing something horrible to him like giving him medicine or trying to bathe him. This stage lasted about 6 months but is probably remembered more because he was always a gentle man, very very strong but always gentle. We had the "walking with very small steps stage" before the finally "can't walk stage."

He had a great set of lungs and bellowed lustily when showered. The happiest stage was "we are in the car and that means they are taking me home stage." We would get into the car when his wanting to go home (even when we were home) became truly upsetting and drive around for a while. When getting back, he would sometimes recognize the house. We always prayed really, really hard that he would recognize the fence or house on return.

For about two years we had been keeping a chart, originally to record his fluid intake because we couldn't pick out exactly what he was having. Gradually over time the chart fleshed out to a full-blown medical history that any major hospital would be proud to call its own. From the count of fluid, the information grew to take in food eaten, medication taken, dressings to wounds, what position he was put to bed in last, when he urinated, when he defecated, when he complained of pain, doctors visits and their outcome, behavioral changes and of course a few Ahhhhhhhhh!!!!! words from Mum and me as well as a couple of funny anecdotes. The chart was a godsend later on dealing with the doctor. We both found our memory of incidents was questionable and couldn't agree when things happened. It is much easier to refer to a daily chart kept, especially when dealing with what pain Dad had and when and what we did to alleviate it. I would recommend that anyone caring for their loved one at home to start a chart.

The biggest frustration for Mum and I as carers was the inability to get him to eat. The anxiety and his being upset or him getting up and down all day, not being able to sleep, changing countless wet beds, monitoring him for infection, dressing bed sores, finding things to perk his interest, bathing, dressing, walking, sitting with him holding hands when he couldn't communicate, watch him get more frustrated himself when he couldn't tell us something he so badly wanted to say was accepted and dealt with. Not being able to get him to eat or drink was the last thing we found hard to accept. That acceptance only came about a week or two before he died.

The last few months of his life were generally waking up, being fed, and sitting with his eyes closed or being popped back into bed to sleep. Gradually refusing to eat, we found we were only able to get him to drink between 600ml and one liter of fluid a day. He was sleeping approximately sixteen hours a day. In the last month fluid intake slipped to approximately 200ml per day and sleeping 20 hours. On the 14th June 2001, Dad slipped into a coma and we spent the next 2 days keeping him clean and dry and comfortable. He required no more morphine, no more food, no more fluid. We used a small pump bottle to spray a mist of water into his mouth to keep it moist. We measured the spray and figured we were giving him .05ml each time. We endeavored to spray his mouth every 15 minutes. *I wished he would push his cup across the table and say "cups empty."*

The last thing Dad said to me was "you're a bloody mongrel bastard." Now that may upset someone else. I was, at the time, changing his position and think I hurt him. Just goes to prove that even close to death, he was still willing to stand up for himself—I hope I'm up to the challenge at that stage myself.

I was going to write down from his chart the last week of his life, but there are some things a carer must find out by themselves and some carers may not yet be ready for that just yet. Besides, Dad is entitled for some privacy and definitely his dignity. I will always "see" Dad as a stockman and family man, fencing the paddocks or in the house drinking coffee. Perhaps dropping his false teeth out in clacking them together to get a two-year-old to shriek with laughter. I think I have inherited his instincts, his love of life, and his sense of the ridiculous.

Frank Burnham died on the 16th June 2001 aged 84-years-old.

FAREWELL © *F.J.Burnham*

Come, dry that silent tear.
I need none but you to remember me.
Maybe in some not too distant time
Our empty selves shall meet and kind reach out to kind
From those dark sub-conscious deeps
Of kindred souls and minds;

And if it be
That we were meant to meet again
I would not change one whit
Of our past together, save
This last parting's pain.

Dear Dad.

I want to write you a letter. I love you but I don't want you to have Alzheimer's disease because it makes you not what I know you to be. I glad you are dead and that your suffering is over.

Lots of love, Rose xxxxx

*　　*　　*

From Mum:

A little thing was my introduction to this dreadful disease. Frank was trying to put a bolt on a door—just six screws and the job would be done. He couldn't work out where the bolt should be on the door or how the catch would be until I held the bolt and said put the screws in. I lined up the catch, he put in the screws and it was finished. He gave me a hug and said, "There's nothing that we can't do together." This was his usual comment whenever we worked together. I put the incident out of my mind—he was always working long hours on too little sleep.

Frank was a clever man, poet and writer, with several prizes in competitions that he'd entered. "One day I'll publish all my writing and poetry." We'd sit and talk about it and look up publishers. "As soon as you get them all typed up properly," I'd say. They were in a mess, mostly typed or written on pink or green paper that he worked on until he felt the piece was right. Some were transferred into proper manuscript form.

He was also a painter. How I envied his painting straight from his mind, no copying from a picture, as I had to do, or waiting for a teacher to give him suggestions on what to do next. After a while I started to wonder if something was wrong, as his painting seemed to get more simple and childish. He had difficulty in working and the paintings didn't seem right. His writing seemed to be suffering too. He would write the same poem over and over on scraps of paper. His spelling was not good any longer. He missed words or letters and sometimes whole lines.

Now he was hiding things—silly things—paper, pencils, knives that he'd sharpened. All pens were now called pencils. Tools were hidden. Saws and secateurs from the shed were hidden in his study. Things of mine disappeared too until, at last, I started putting things away from him so I'd know where they were when I needed them.

By now we'd sold our old large rambling home on a large block for a smaller home on a normal house block. Frank would start to mow the lawn then take the mower in the shed to fix it. We ended up with bits of mowers all over the workbench with pieces of weed eaters and other tools mixed up together. His electric typewriter ended up with pieces taken off, too. In the end I started taking anything to be mended into a workshop instead of letting Frank do the repairs. Diesel had been put in one mower, oil into the petrol of another. I was getting a bit cranky with all this. "What the hell is he up to?" I'd think. I had never heard of Alzheimer's disease.

When we were at the doctors one day I mentioned that Frank seemed to be getting forgetful. He was given tablets to take. Natural herbs were also suggested. These didn't seem to be having any effect, and when we were at the doctors again I said so. There were tests done after this and eventually we were told of Alzheimer's. We thought we could cope with this disease; after all we'd coped with all the things that had gone wrong during our life together. We were so innocent. We weren't even given a full rundown on just what could happen over the years to come.

I'd get cranky with his "deliberate" annoying forgetfulness. He got quieter, thought I had stopped loving him, and thought he was a nuisance. I know this because I found it written on a scrap of paper since his death.

I got doctor to refuse him a license after he'd driven down the wrong way on a divided highway, frightening both my mother and myself. He stayed at home more when I went shopping, either in his study or lying down sleeping. He couldn't go out on his own, as he was so forgetful of what he was going to do or where he was. Even in the house he needed watching, as he could not do things properly for himself. Now I made sure he had some identification on him at all times. I'd started marking all his clothes. I was even locking the doors so he couldn't wander off on his own. I'd also had another talk with doctor and could see that things were not going to get any better.

At this time I found prayer a big help. I said the Serenity prayer so often, it's a wonder the words didn't vanish off the small plaque that I read them from. Patience was something I prayed hard for, and eventually it came. I also gained acceptance that I was going to lose Frank and all I had to do was to try to help him as long as I could.

My daughter and her family came back to Brisbane to help us, and bought a property close by so we could live with them in the country, as we preferred to do. Frank was still doing things for himself. Who cared if he wanted to wear clothes inside out or in the wrong places? He took a fancy to one of my pink jumpers and wore it. We loved him and tried to make things easier for him. His fifteen—and sixteen-year-old granddaughters were very good. They played with him and talked to him. This was a relief for me as I could leave him for short times knowing he was safe. The Blue Nurses were good, giving Rose and I respite for a few hours so we could go shopping. As we were building a small flat on the end of their house, there were many things we had to look at or buy. We tried taking Frank out with us at first but he hated it and wanted to go home. Crowds seemed to frighten him and noise drove him mad. Try this: If you are in a shopping center, even a small one, stop, close your eyes and listen. You'll be surprised at just how noisy it is.

By now Frank was in a wheelchair most of the time. We were feeding him, bathing, and dressing him. He'd just about stopped talking at all. The Blue Nurses came three times a week to shower him. At these times he was very vocal and called poor Peter some dreadful names. Peter agreed with him and went on talking about football and other things.

One of Frank's medicines to quiet him, Serenace (haloperidol in the United States), had the opposite effect and made him almost impossible to deal with or even be near. Our doctor was very good— we could talk to him and tried other means take away Frank's anxiety and confusion. In the end Frank was on Risperidol, a Fentanyl patch for pain, and morphine mix for breakthrough pain.

We were feeding him Ensure puddings, (a type of custard) supplied by the Department of Veterans Affairs and giving him Resource fruit juices also supplied by DVA. We did try mashed potatoes but in the end he wouldn't touch them.

Frank got bedsores on his feet, but we managed to keep them under some control. They were painful, his hips and arms ached. The only way we knew this was from his cries of pain when we moved him. He preferred to lie on his right side and when we turned him he wouldn't settle for long. For the last few weeks I often sat beside his bed praying his life would end and all his pain would be gone.

On what was to be his last day I sat and said aloud to him "It's time to go love, time to leave me, one day we'll be together again. Go, it's time to go." A few hours later he died while our two daughters, Rose and Phyllis, stood with me beside his bed. One of our sons had left a few minutes before and another arrived just after Frank died. A couple of quiet breaths and our life together were really over.

I have wonderful memories of my scallywag of a husband and a painting that I did of him years ago. He had turned to me and smiled and now I can speak to him whenever I want. I'm sure he gives me a cheeky wink. I know I always feel better as our eyes meet and can't suppress a smile. This is my favorite poem. It was written by him.

Forever. © *F.J.Burnham*

Soft as the kiss of a moonbeam
Sweet as the first breath of Spring
Stronger are bonds that bind us
Than those of our service and ring.
Bright, comes each day to our greeting
Each day a new treasure trove
Fond, are our memories of meeting
Sweet were those dreams that we wove

And this one, I trust, will come true
That through all Time in it's fleeting
I will walk hand and with you.

(From Val, his wife)

I don't think I can add anything to that except "Frank I love you and though I miss you, your love still surrounds me as warmth and peace. One day I know we'll be together again and "till then Goodnight my love."

Val

SHIRLEY

Nothing Par for the Course

by Laurie

Mom was a rock. She was resilient, strong, and determined in a way that belied her petite frame.

One of six children, she grew up poor on a family farm. Her father spent much of his time in the hospital suffering from poorly controlled epilepsy. Her self-reliance began early, and by high school she was working part-time to help support the family while she completed high school. Yet she triumphed.

She went on to become a legal secretary, a job requiring deftness, organization, and multiple other skills. It was while she was a secretary in the legal department of the company she worked for that she met my father, who was chief engineer for the company. She continued to work after they married until she became pregnant with me. She was a stay-at-home Mom for twelve years until she chose to return to work part-time, much to my father's chagrin. An old-fashioned man in some ways, Dad thought I was too young not to have Mom at home all the time.

She worked for two years, but the conflicts her working caused resulted in her quitting to return to being at home full-time. Sadly, my parents were ultimately unable to work through their differences and divorced when I was nineteen.

The divorce began a time of readjustment for all of us. Mom moved to our house at the lake, where she remains to this day. I moved out on my own. More difficult for all of us, we were all reeling from the divorce and associated rifts it caused between all of us. I was essentially estranged from Mom for two years, and longer from Dad. I think we all just needed our own space and time to sort through the aftereffects of the divorce, and to create new paths for ourselves.

Mom had always been independent, and true to form she eventually picked herself up, dusted herself off, and got on with her life. A doctor's appointment had revealed high cholesterol. Unlike many who don't make many changes when discovering a health issue over which they can exert control, Mom made significant life changes. She started eating an incredibly healthy diet and she made sure that she got sufficient exercise. As part of that change, she took up golf. Little did she know that, thanks to her newfound penchant for golf, she would meet the man who was to become her husband and, now, her caregiver.

My future stepfather was at a conference held near where Mom played golf, and they were at the conference center's restaurant at the same time. Mom overheard him and his co-attendees talking about what to do in the area. Mom had always loved socializing, and was unendingly friendly. She knew the area well, so chimed in to offer information about the area. The rest is history. They married in 1986.

Life was good for a few years. My grandmother, who had always been the glue that held everything together and was my best friend, was diagnosed with Alzheimer's in 1990 and had to move to a nursing home in 1993. She was 82-years-old when she was diagnosed. Mom spent much of her time caring for my grandmother, even in the nursing home where Mom continued to care for her daily. I was living in Florida when the diagnosis came, and moved back North soon afterward. I didn't really understand the diagnosis or Alzheimer's. To me, it was a case of senility that had taken root in this beloved person.

It was in 1994 that I first became concerned about Mom. She was visiting me at home after I had minor surgery. We talked and laughed as usual. At one point in the conversation, Mom stopped talking, clearly forgetting what she was saying. We laughed it off— we all have those lapses at times. We said our goodbyes and Mom left for her home about 45-minutes away from mine. About ten minutes later my doorbell rang and, much to my surprise, it was Mom. She looked like she was in shock, like a ghost. When I asked her what was wrong, she replied, "How do I get out of here?"

I was alarmed. Mom knew my area and her own like the back of her hand. I gave her the simple directions, which sparked recognition and she appeared to then remember how to wend her way home, reassuring me that she would be fine driving home. I again became alarmed when I attempted to call her at home for two hours and she didn't answer. Finally, she answered sounding completely spent. She told me that she'd fallen asleep when she got home and was totally exhausted, sounding so on the phone. Mom was 58-years-old.

My stepfather traveled a lot for work and was typically gone for most of the week every week. He and I spoke about the incident and my concern. He hadn't noticed any problems with Mom. A loving husband since the day that he and Mom married, my stepfather didn't want to hear it. "There's nothing wrong with your mother, I'd know if there was," was his response. Still concerned, I guess I let it go and chalked it up to being an anomaly or thought Mom might even have had a mini-stroke. Our conversations and interactions after that were normal, at least for a brief period.

Then three months after that initial incident my aunt, who lives ten-minutes from Mom and my stepfather, called. She was clearly concerned about Mom. She had given Mom directions to a new hairdresser and got a call from that hairdresser after Mom's appointment. Mom couldn't remember her way home and couldn't remember her address. My aunt had to meet Mom at the hairdresser's and lead her home. My stepfather still couldn't acknowledge that there was a problem, brushing off our concerns.

But I began to notice other changes. Mom had always been particular about her appearance, always wearing makeup and maintaining carefully manicured nails. While she was not unkempt, I noticed that she stopped wearing makeup and her manicured nails were a thing of the past. And she started wearing hats or even wigs sometimes. Mom never wore hats. This woman who had always looked so put-together no longer did.

At the same time I was pregnant with my daughter and developed preeclampsia. Now, Mom and I had grown close over the years. We were close when I was a child and became even more so as we both aged. I was hospitalized for a month and Mom and my stepfather only visited once after my daughter was born. Mom didn't even call the hospital. Whenever I called her she sounded far away and vague. I noticed that my stepfather began doing more and more for Mom. Even calling their house meant that he was always the one to pick up the phone where before it had always been Mom—a small change but a change nonetheless. I was worried about so many things, my baby, my health and the changes in my mother.

As is so common with Alzheimer's, things weren't static and Mom did have her good moments. She wanted to come to my daughter's first well-baby visit and did just that. We had a lovely day. Mom even drove herself and did fine through the whole day. I did notice the changes in her appearance, though, even on that lovely day.

Yet another incident again led to my aunt and me increasing our concerns about Mom. Mom called my aunt, hysterically claiming there was a bear in the yard. There was an animal in the yard, but it wasn't a bear—it was a raccoon. I don't know if she was hallucinating or couldn't find the right word for "raccoon," but it was alarming.

Mom was alone a lot due to my stepfather's travels for work. We even began to wonder if she had begun drinking a lot during all of that time alone. I had no idea that we should even consider Alzheimer's as a possibility. I was so naive. I thought Alzheimer's was something people only got when they were in their eighties. I was naive about what was going on with my grandmother, too. I just thought it was a case of senility.

My grandmother died in April of 1996. Mom's condition changed almost overnight after my grandmother's death. She developed aphasia, speaking in only one-word utterances. Her attention and concentration were, by all appearances, gone. She went rapidly downhill and never came out of it.

Finally, in late 1996, my stepfather acknowledged that there was something wrong. He and Mom were on the golf course, a place that they frequented. Mom had no idea where she was.

I don't know what it is that caused him to deny all of the problems she had been having up to that point. Denial maybe. If that's what it was, it's such a little word for such a big issue!

I really felt I needed to assert myself a little at that point, telling my stepfather if he didn't take Mom to a doctor that I would. He reluctantly agreed, though he felt that I was being overdramatic about the whole thing. Sadly for me, I wasn't included in the visits to the doctors. My stepfather was her next of kin and had power of attorney, so there was little I could do to change that situation. He clearly understood to some degree that she was going downhill since he did have the foresight to have her sign important documents like power of attorney and a living will. He finally took the big step of getting a formal diagnosis, first taking her to a general practitioner, who referred them to a neurologist.

Mom was diagnosed with Alzheimer's disease in January of 1997. She was 60-years-old. I was numb when I heard the diagnosis, a numbness that has never really worn off.

There were so many changes. Mom and my stepfather would still come to visit us, and Mom loved holding the baby. But she called my daughter, "the baby," and my name morphed into "the girl." My stepfather became "Daddy." Mom would pick things up and put them in her mouth. Once when I was in the kitchen making a salad, Mom came into the kitchen and tried to grab the knife. Mom was a wonderful cook and loved to cook, passing along many of those skills to me. All of those little losses added up.

Mom started to get worse. She became incontinent, which I discovered only because I thought I detected the outline of a diaper under her clothes. She became combative and aggressive at times. She even twice struck my daughter, which came out of the blue. She would approach my daughter smiling and with open arms. And then bam, she hit her. At one point, my stepfather and Mom showed up and he was wearing a long-sleeved shirt on a hot day. I questioned him about it and he lifted his sleeves to show horrible black and blue bruises and scratches, all caused by my mother.

She was on Aricept for a while and was in the clinical trials of Exelon, which I didn't think helped much but my stepfather felt did help to slow the progression. Ironically, the clinical trials were held at Yale University, where I work as a senior administrator. My work at Yale University has me working side-by-side with researchers and I know that there are new discoveries in Alzheimer's almost every day, so it gives me some hope for the future of this disease. I think there is a reason I am working at Yale and involved with people on the cutting edge of this illness.

Despite all of those difficulties and challenges, my stepfather was and is an attentive caregiver. He treats Mom like gold. If only he could let the rest of us in—I miss my mother and being able to be part of the decisions and all of the little chores that would make me feel like I was a part of her life now. Still, he has taken good care of her throughout. Even as early as 1996, Mom would become hysterical if my stepfather was out of her sight for even a few seconds. He would have to take her to the bathroom when they went out, and she would scream at him and hit him. But he continued to care for her diligently. He took her shopping at Talbots and they regularly went out to eat, something that both of them always enjoyed. He would take her to get her hair done every couple of weeks and tended to her every need. She lost so much confidence in herself and became so insecure; my stepfather became her security blanket. I want and need to be a bigger part of her care and sometimes resent being shut out, but have to commend my stepfather for the loving care he has provided Mom. And there have still been special times together, though sometimes they're bittersweet.

One day I drove up to her house and my stepfather had told her I was coming. As my car pulled into the driveway my mother ran out of the house and into my arms. She held me so tight and wouldn't let go. I think she knew.

I remember when Princess Di died in 1997, Mom came to visit. Princess Di's funeral was on the television, and it was clear that Mom didn't understand what she was watching. She was becoming a shell of herself. She had always been so animated but that part of her personality was gone. I knew that I was losing her. I think on some level she knew it too. I was determined to make the best of the times we had together.

Christmas of 2001 is a memory that stands out in my mind. Somehow I knew that it would be the last Christmas that my mother would enjoy at my house. I used her old recipes and made her favorite dishes. She seemed to enjoy herself. She and my stepfather were leaving for Florida the next day. They had a house there and spent the winters in that house. My stepfather tried to assure me that she would be fine and they would be back in the spring.

In February of 2002, he called to tell me that mom had suffered a stroke after having a virus. He thought the sneezing and coughing had brought on the stroke. He had found her on the floor with her eyes rolled back in her head. She was put on anti-seizure medicine but within a few days she had another seizure. They returned home to Connecticut and my aunt called me to update me on Mom's condition. Mom was now in a wheelchair. No one had wanted to tell me. My mother was no longer able to walk without my stepfather standing behind her, holding her, and moving her feet with his own. And Mom couldn't remember how to feed herself.

Families all have such different issues and configurations to cope with at times like this. My stepfather and I have always gotten along. During Mom's illness, he has felt the need to be in control of everything, from the smallest details to the bigger issues. As a result, I've been shut out of most of Mom's care. I feel like I'm on the outside looking in. The same is true for my aunt. He updates us by letter, usually to me with copies to my aunt and his children by his previous marriage. One letter was particularly horrific.

I arrived home from work during the summer of 2002 and checked my mail, only to find one of my stepfather's updates. He and Mom had been to the doctor. He informed me in the letter that in that neurologist's appointment, the doctor informed them that Mom was in the end-stages of Alzheimer's and had about six months to a year to live. My stepfather reported that the doctor's advice was that "the best thing for everyone is to let go" and that the end would probably come in the form of "respiratory or renal failure." It was all very cut-and-dried, very businesslike. It really felt like none of this was real—I was receiving this news about my adored mother in a letter with copies to his children. My aunt wasn't copied on that letter. I was so hurt and angry, and I have to admit that my trust in him wavered at that point.

I was so upset I couldn't work the next day and drove to the lake house. I confronted my stepfather about delivering that news by letter and reiterated my need to speak with the doctor. I also wanted to talk about her future care, including bringing in either hospice or hiring a nurse for some homecare. I didn't know what to expect, and neither did my stepfather. What would he do if Mom went into respiratory failure? Did he know how to take a blood pressure? There were so many problems that needed to be addressed and my stepfather didn't want to address them. He refused to consider bringing in someone else to help care for Mom.

I finally called the neurologist in an attempt to arrange a meeting between my stepfather, the neurologist, and myself. I was told that, as next-of-kin, only my stepfather could arrange the meeting. This time I insisted and he relented. We met on my forty-second birthday. In the meeting, I again repeated my belief that Mom should have hospice care, and the neurologist agreed. My stepfather agreed to the extent that from then on, Mom has had a hospice nurse visit once a week for the last two years.

And my stepfather continues his loving care. Now, two years after we received the news that Mom had only a short time to live, Mom is still with us. He and I don't have heart-to-heart talks about her or anything else, but I see the care that he provides, continuing with buying her beautiful clothes and regular visits to the hairdresser. He continues to move her feet with his, even after them falling together a couple of times. Mom is tiny, weighing only 110-pounds, but she is deadweight. Their love is deep and lasting, and it shows in the care that he gives Mom every moment.

And now, two years after hearing that Mom would soon die, I also look back over some of the moments we have shared during her illness and so many come to mind. I remember a Mother's Day card I gave her a few years ago. I could tell that she couldn't read the card so I read it out loud to her. Nevertheless, she reached for her reading glasses and put them on. It was a very emotional card. As I read the words I could see her glasses fog up. We were both laughing and crying. I'll never forget that moment in time. And the time she ran into my arms holding me so tight, the times we had before the Alzheimer's began to steal her away are all things I will always remember. I'll remember them for her, and for me.

There are days when I get through without tears and other days when the simplest little thing will just tear me apart. It is hard to accept that my daughter, who is eight-years-old now, will never have memories of my mother before Alzheimer's. It is hard wondering if someday I will suffer the same fate, a thought that also scares my daughter. I worry about the fact that early-onset Alzheimer's has a stronger hereditary component, but take some comfort from the fact that all of Mom's siblings are alive and well. I have thought about whether I would want to know my future if a definitive test for Alzheimer's existed. I can honestly say I don't know. I suppose there would be value in knowing and preparing for that future. Then again, I don't know if I could fully live life if I had the knowledge that Alzheimer's was in my future.

I would tell anyone who is struggling with a family member with this illness to please look into a support group. For me the answer was an online support group. I was afraid that, sitting face-to-face with other caregivers I would lose it. Online, I was more at ease expressing that emotion and could be as open as I wanted without fear that I'd be sitting in a group of people sobbing. Deb and Rose were the first two people I met when I found the Massachusetts General Hospital chat room for Alzheimer's caregivers. I don't know what I would have done if I hadn't found someone to talk to who understood the way this illness takes your loved one away a little bit at a time.

If I had five minutes to talk to Mom, five minutes in which she was clear and could understand, I'd simply tell her that I love her. That's what I want her to know, to always know, and to take with her.

JACK

A Sailor's Last Voyage

by Deborah Uetz

Jack was my dad. He and my mother were high school sweethearts. I was their firstborn and in preparation for my birth my parents began building their house. They had been living in the basement, which they had dug with shovels. They added the upper part of the house when they found out Mom was expecting. They built it as they could pay for each load of lumber. Dad had never built a house or wired one but that didn't slow him down. My mother still resides in the house they built together. Later they had two sons, Keith and David.

Dad had always been a good provider having worked in an oil refinery for eighteen years and later becoming a carpenter. He was a WWII Veteran who left high school his senior year to fight the war. Looking back at the old black and white photos of Dad in his sailor suit he looks like a little boy, so thin and young. Those four years he spent in the Philippines and other hot spots in the war made quite an impression upon him. They were his longest lasting memories.

My dad never had a memory of his mother. She died when he was three years old. Strangely enough one of the first unusual things he did when he became ill was ask where his mother was.

Dad's father built racecars and Dad and I shared a love of cars. Each time Dad was ready to buy a new car he would take me along to the showroom. Those trips to the showroom are some of my fondest memories of my father and me.

Dad loved his independence. He was never one to ask anyone for help. Instead he would lend a hand to anyone. Dad couldn't sit still a minute. He would almost seem to be in two places at once with his constant activities. He would be mowing the yard one minute and working in his garden the next.

He had a keen sense of humor and enjoyed a joke or a cartoon more than most people. I remember going to the movie theatre with him when I was a child. Back then the main feature would be preceded by a cartoon. Dad would belly laugh so loud it was embarrassing! His sense of humor was among the last pieces of his personality to leave him.

About ten years before his Alzheimer's diagnosis he had been diagnosed with diabetes. Immediately he stopped smoking, followed a rigid diet and began a walking regimen of four miles a day. He seemed to be in tiptop shape. The first thing we noticed was he was complaining of dizziness. He complained about feeling off balance if he looked up. We weren't alarmed.

He began repeating the same stories or showing us the same old photographs. We didn't think much about it. It just seemed as though he was excited to see us and just didn't realize he had already shared them with us.

My mother often complained that he didn't listen. She would tell him something and later he denied having been told. This "not listening" situation was becoming a real source of irritation for her. Not only did he claim that she had not told him, he would be upset that she hadn't told him.

He began making driving mistakes, becoming confused at intersections or lane changes. Turn signals were often forgotten. Still it was not evident that he had a problem. We just thought he was a little absentminded. In hindsight perhaps we should have taken it more seriously.

An incident one spring morning sent my father to the emergency room. He was sitting at the dining room table when my mother noticed him staring into space. He didn't respond to her voice and his hands were limp in his lap. By the time the ambulance arrived at the emergency room he had come out of it and seemed fine. It was decided that he had experienced a blood sugar drop, due to his diabetes and he was sent home. Seeing an ambulance pull up to their house and load Dad on a stretcher was such an unimaginable thing. He was the healthiest person I had ever known, aside from his diabetes.

A follow up doctor's appointment was scheduled and the doctor ordered blood work and an M.R.I. My mother had explained to the doctor that there had been other things going on, the dizziness, etc. and she asked the doctor to rule out anything serious.

By the time the tests were back Dad was becoming more confused. He called his grandchildren by the wrong names and had difficulty remembering the day of the week. My mother began to post the day of the week on a bulletin board. He checked the board each morning to see what day it was. He began keeping notes of our names and relationship to him. He would put a little piece of paper on the front of the refrigerator. The note read: "Deb, my daughter, Ed (my husband), Keith my son and David my son."

These notes made it clear just how much he had forgotten. We found more lists of our names lying about the house and others he kept in his shirt pocket.

Dad's naps became longer and more frequent. He didn't show the same interest in activities. He had always loved to be on the go but now he opted to stay at home. His favorite leisure time activity was going to a Riverboat Casino nearby. Even that lost its appeal. He seemed sad.

This depression and an increase in agitation appeared early on. He was moody and easily upset. His mood would change suddenly and was usually worse after a nap. He was like a different person when he woke up, very disoriented. We didn't know that all of these pieces were part of a puzzle. We just didn't put it all together. Dad was always seeing the negative side of things and he seemed short-tempered. When he refused to do things that he had once enjoyed my mother thought he was just being obstinate. At our insistence he agreed to see a doctor.

I'll never forget when he walked out of the doctor's office. My mother was walking behind him. Dad walked out of the office, looked at me and made a gesture as if he were cutting his throat. He was grinning but I could tell he was troubled.

I asked what happened. He said "I'm gonna kill your mother!" He was still grinning. "They want to send me for tests!" He grumbled. I asked what kind of tests and he said they had ordered an M.R.I. He was scared. All the way home he teased my mom about getting him into the situation.

The agitation became worse. It was like walking on eggshells being around Dad. He would shout at all of us. Since we didn't realize that he was sick it was difficult to be around him. He would make mistakes and then get angry if they were noticed. My mother insisted he go through with the tests. I know that Dad only agreed because he thought that would be the end of it. Instead it was only the beginning.

After having seen his physician and completing a series of tests Dad was referred to a neurologist. My father, mother and I went into the small examining room, not knowing what to expect.

Dad sat on the examining table and the doctor engaged him in casual conversation. Dad was obviously having trouble coming up with the right words. The doctor told us that the M.R.I. had shown some atrophy (shrinkage) of the brain and two sites of possible small strokes. Everything else looked normal.

The neurologist asked Dad to write a sentence, tell time, draw a clock face showing a specific time, count backwards by sevens and he asked him to remember three objects. Those objects were rose, thumb and ball. Dad repeated the three objects several times trying to commit them to memory.

The doctor asked Dad about problems that he had been having. He could only remember the dizziness. We described the changes in his mood. It was uncomfortable to talk about his behavior changes with Dad in the room. We didn't want to embarrass him. He didn't seem to even notice as we spoke about his increased agitation and confusion.

Finally the doctor asked Dad to name the three objects. Dad named one; the other two were gone from his memory. The doctor said that he believed him to be in stage 4 or 5 of the seven stages of Alzheimer's disease. Dad was exhibiting some memory and speech deficits.

Dad spoke up, not reacting at all to the diagnosis, and asked if he could still drive. The driving issue had been a real source of distress for him. He resented having anyone question his driving ability.

The neurologist agreed to let him drive for a while longer but only if he stayed within the boundaries of our little community. Dad agreed enthusiastically. There was no follow-up visit scheduled. We were told to just go on as usual but keep an eye on him for more changes in behavior and thinking ability. I remember feeling apprehensive about the fact that there was no follow up appointment. Basically we were on our own.

By the time we walked the twenty-five or so feet to our parked car Dad was insisting that the doctor had not set any limit on his driving. He didn't remember any of that conversation.

Of all the struggles that lay ahead one of the most difficult for Dad was getting him to stop driving. My family learned the hard way that it is not a good idea to have car keys or even house keys in plain view. The sight of the car keys would cause Dad to begin the argument about driving all over again. We learned to keep keys out of sight.

Initially Dad's driving mistakes involved forgetting to use turn signals and being confused at intersections and turn lanes. There were many close calls but never an accident. Nearly every time he ran an errand for my mother he would come back with a story about someone nearly running into him. We didn't realize at the time that he was most likely the one causing the near misses.

I told my mom that I wouldn't ride with him any longer. She was upset by my comment. My mother doesn't drive so their independence hinged upon his being able to drive. He was still driving when he was having hallucinations. He could have swerved off the road to avoid something that wasn't real.

There were so many subtle changes. On the day of Dad's M.R.I. test I saw a side of him I had never seen. There was a waiting area just outside of the testing area. Dad was like a little boy sitting nervously and asking me every few minutes whether he should use the rest room one more time. He was so childlike and unsure of himself. It was such a role reversal. I was amazed by his lack of confidence.

Dad was becoming more obviously bewildered with each passing day. My mother tried to help him with his puzzlement by giving him simple commands to follow. She would say "put the book on the table" and Dad would lay it on the floor. Over and over she tried to get him to follow the command but each time he laid it on the floor. The volume of the television began to make him nervous. He was once a very social person but being in a group of people began to make him uneasy.

In September Mom and Dad came to my house for Mom's birthday. We had a birthday cake and I had decorated my living room with streamers of crape paper. Dad didn't seem to understand what all the decorations were for. He kept looking at the cake and the crape paper and just seemed puzzled by it all.

Dad didn't know who my brother was. He asked my mom who he was and she said, "He's your son." Dad's reply was "I don't know that!" When he made that comment at the birthday party I think we all took a deep breath and realized how far he had slipped.

Dad always loved to watch sports on television. He had lost the ability to understand sports. He couldn't follow the plot of anything on television. One evening he was watching football and said, "They just run down there and all fall down!" He would watch baseball and think that every batter was Mark McGuire. Nothing would hold his attention very long. His long walks had helped keep his blood sugar level low but the walks were becoming a problem. He was at risk of becoming lost even in familiar places.

On September 9, 1999 my dad received the diagnosis. That date is etched into my memory like no other. We were numb, neither grateful nor relieved. Just numb.

I am not sure where the early stages stop and the middle stages begin. Things blend together and awful days are followed by better ones so you are always left wondering where your loved one is in the progression of the disease.

Dad began to hide his wallet and other belongings. Much of the day was spent searching for them. He was waking up from his naps in a horrible state, grouchy and unbearable. He was accusing my mom of stealing things from him and it seemed he would try to provoke a fight with her.

Dad began to believe that he lived next door to his house and he was afraid that someone would catch him in the wrong house. He would look out the window at the house next door and say, "I'm supposed to be over there!"

My relationship with my dad was not as close as I wish it had been. I loved him but hadn't spent much time having real conversations with him. He was always busy with work or projects around the house. The best day I ever spent with him was, oddly enough, when I was in my thirties and we were sitting up all night at my grandmother's bedside. My grandmother, his mother-in-law, was gravely ill and Dad and I volunteered to spend the night in her hospital room. My grandmother slept throughout the day and night so that left my dad and I to fill the silence. We talked the whole night.

He told me about riding a bicycle all the way to another town, along with his best friend. It was nighttime so they taped a flashlight onto the front of the bike. He told me about being in the islands during his Navy years. We laughed about things that happened on vacations when I was little. The next morning I remember Dad telling the other relatives "My daughter and I spent the whole night talking."

I wouldn't take a million dollars for that night in grandma's hospital room but I would give anything if I could go back in time and have long talks with him. By the time we realized what was happening to him it was too late. I wish I had asked more questions about his life while he was able to tell me.

The middle stages were a time of problem solving. There were practical matters to consider and act on almost daily. Dad became increasingly agitated in the evenings, insisting he was late for work. He would walk out of his bedroom dressed in his finest clothes ready to go to an event which had occurred weeks before. The disappointment in his face was heartbreaking.

He continued to attempt to get the car keys and a few times he did. He would start the car with my mother hanging onto the car door, begging him not to leave. He wanted to get away. We didn't know where he wanted to go and I don't think he did either.

Dad became more obsessed with hiding things. He would hide money in "invisible mouse holes" and then go looking for it. He would get down on his hands and knees and rub the carpeting looking for the hole that had "closed up." He also hid the mail, money intended for paying bills; anything he felt was valuable to him. Hours were spent trying to imagine where he had hidden things.

Some people who suffer from dementia have auditory or visual hallucinations. The hallucinations were among the most upsetting times during his illness. Not only was he seeing things that were not real he was also frightened by many of those hallucinations. He would tell us "look over there. Do you see all those cats?" There were no cats. He saw bandits in the kitchen, little people climbing out of his magazine rack. He thought he saw my mother standing next to him when she was actually no where near him. He would become upset believing that she had walked away. All the while he had been in a room alone.

Dad believed that he and my mother were getting a divorce. He told his neighbor about it. Later he didn't believe they had ever been married. My mother would take out their marriage certificate to prove it to him but he didn't believe her.

When dad began showing symptoms I started keeping a journal. Each day was so demanding and topsy turvy that I found a journal was the best way to keep track of his needs and changes in his behavior. The journal began a few weeks after his diagnosis. The middle stages of Alzheimer's disease are usually the longest. I found myself writing in my journal almost daily during the middle stages. I would suggest keeping a journal not only as a record keeping device but also as a means to express your feelings. There were times when my journal reflected a sense of anguish, sometimes anger and other times sad reflections of opportunities missed. I have removed a lot of entries because they were very private.

JOURNAL

OCTOBER 2 (THREE WEEKS AFTER HIS DIAGNOSIS)

Dad's medicine was increased. He is confused all the time. He doesn't understand how the days of the week work and he can't tell time. He looked at the checkbook and became very angry with my mother for writing checks. He thinks she is writing checks to people he doesn't know. She has had to take over all of their financial dealings. She has to do it behind his back. I imagine that this only increases his paranoia but she has no other choice. He doesn't recognize the names of places that the checks are written to and thinks they are stealing his money.

It is quite common for Alzheimer's patients to believe someone is stealing from them or hiding things from them. It is important that you not react in a defensive or angry manner.

October 4

Dad tried to put on two tee shirts. He urinated on the floor last night. Mom is crying and says that she has already lost my dad. Dad has been hallucinating today. He thought he saw a man in the bedroom and he was talking to a little girl who wasn't there. He was trying to show the little girl a picture in a magazine. Dad has started walking on his tiptoes. One day he opened the clothes dryer and asked my Mom where he would come out if he went in through the clothes dryer.

Even though the hallucinations are upsetting to witness it is important that you do not react in a way that will increase the Alzheimer's

*patient's fear and confusion. Never argue with them about what is real
and what is not real. Be comforting and calm.*

October 5

Dad is still seeing people who aren't there. He thought he saw
each of us getting in and out of his bed all night. He saw a rabbit
hopping in the yard but when we looked it was only a potted
plant. He fell going up some stairs today. I am very upset. I am
angry that my dad can't grow old with my mother. I am jealous of
people whose loved ones can be cured of their diseases. My dad
will never get better than he is today. My mother-in-law is
rehabilitating from a fall. She is living in a nursing home but making
plans to return to her own home. I love her and I'm excited that
she is getting better but some part of me is also jealous. I want
Dad to get better but he never will. This is a one-way trip.

*Feeling as if you are loosing them a tiny bit at a time is the kind of
emotional response that you can write about in your journal.*

October 6

Dad tried to put his under shorts on over his pants today. He
thinks that I am my Mom's sister. I want my mother to speak to
the doctor about Dad's agitation. She said, "I've been angry more
often than he has." We have tried to talk to her about Alzheimer's
disease but she says we are just telling her these things to hurt her.
I don't know how to get her to read about it. She can't continue to
get angry with him and argue with him.

October 10

Dad asked my mom who my brother is. She explained that he
is his son. Then he said, "Who is his mom?" She said, "I am." My
mom's heart is breaking but she is still in denial. I think on some
level she knows that this can't go on without getting outside help
but she doesn't want to give up yet.

October 11

My dad is asking where his mother is. My dad's mother died when he was three years old. Today his sisters visited him. He asked them if they would call the police if he showed up at their house. They asked why he thought that they would and he said, "Because I'm not supposed to drive." I feel embarrassed for him. His dignity is evaporating.

October 12

Mom and Dad came by my house this afternoon. Dad wouldn't come in. He sat on my porch and told me he was watching a little man run around inside of a tire. There was nothing there. The other day my dad took off walking through a field across from his house. My mother was trying to keep up with him but couldn't. She shouted to him that her back was hurting and to please stop. He wouldn't stop. She is angry because he "doesn't care about her back." I told her that he doesn't understand anymore. He can't process that. I don't think he even understands that she is his wife.

October 13

Dad fell last night. He fell in the bathroom and was shaken but no broken bones. The falls are happening more often. Usually he falls in the bathroom.

I made him a photo album of our family. I labeled each photo "my son, David . . . my daughter Deb, etc." He looked at each photograph and I read him the label under the picture. His eyes were wide with amazement. I had been concerned that the labels on the photographs would insult him. Now I realize that he needed the names printed below the pictures in order to identify us. We keep finding slips of paper with our names written on them. He uses them to remember our names. He also keeps written reminders in his pockets to remind him that I am his daughter, Keith and David are his sons and his wife is named Frances.

Falls become more and more of a possibility as an Alzheimer's patient is unable to comprehend familiar surroundings. They may see a rug on the floor and think it is a hole in the floor. They may misjudge the height of a step. The section on Alzheimer's proofing your home will help avoid some of those situations.

October 14

He tried to start his car today. He tried every key but couldn't get it right. My mother held on to the car door and begged him not to drive. He tries every key he can find to try to start the car, even his door key. This has to stop. He could have driven away dragging my mother. It is becoming clear that mother will not make the hard decisions.

October 15

I begged my Dad for his keys this morning. This was a very painful day. My heart is broken. Mom didn't want me to do it. I knew that as long as there were keys in sight he would continue to try to drive. I went into his house and knelt down beside his chair. I said "Dad you know how much I have always wanted a horse?" He said he did. I said, "There is something I want even more. I want you to give me your car keys." He looked at me for a minute, made me promise not to lose them and then he stood up, took them out of his pocket and handed them to me.

The number of people who continue to drive when they are impaired by dementia is astounding. Far too many people fail to confront the situation and by doing so they put the Alzheimer's sufferer at risk of becoming lost, causing an accident and they put everyone at risk. Don't wait too long to address driving issues.

October 18

We had heavy frost last night and Dad thinks someone has painted the trees. He sees the world through a child's eyes. My brother took his little boy and my dad out to a pumpkin farm today. Before he knew it my dad had crawled into a hay maze. He is becoming a little boy. He is aging backwards.

October 22

It has only been a few weeks since Dad was driving and getting along independently. He is asking us who we are. He wants to shred the books in the bookcase. He made himself a sandwich without anything in between the bread. He thinks his son is his brother and he gets very upset almost every evening.

Getting more agitated late in the day is called Sun Downing.

October 27

Dad was angry all night. He sleeps with a little flashlight because he is afraid of the dark. He shined it in my mom's eyes all night and asked her the time. He thinks he isn't allowed to drive because he is being punished for not sleeping. He is threatening to freeze his bank account and give all of his money to his four-year-old grandson. My mom's health is going down quickly. She watches his every move all day and is awake with him every night.

October 28

Dad thought he saw gangsters in the kitchen. It scared him. He said they were bandits with masks. Mom called to tell me that he has his riding lawn mower out and is trying to use it. It isn't safe for him to be on the mower so I raced down the street and pulled the spark plug loose when he wasn't looking. Almost every day there is another crisis situation. Sometimes there is an hourly dilemma.

October 29

I gathered up 13 knives from my mom's kitchen. She was not happy with me. She thinks it ridiculous that I fear he might hurt her. I left one knife hidden for her to use while cooking. He continues the ritual of hiding his wallet. He and my mother spend the better part of the day looking for things he has hidden. He checks the mail and she has to check to see if he has taken any of it. He keeps saying that he wants to "get away." I am very afraid that he will try to walk or drive away and get lost. He gets angry with Mom for ignoring him. He tells her that he was in the middle of a conversation with her and she just ignores him. This is happening when he is sitting all alone. I guess he "sees" her sitting next to him. Today he was talking to a woman in a red dress that wasn't there.

Every time we try to discuss Alzheimer's proofing the house she says that there isn't any need. Even after all of this my mom thinks Dad is getting better if he has a "good day."

At this point mom and my brother Keith are exhausted as they try to keep up with dad all day and all night. They take turns sitting up all night.

October 30

Dad is trying to hit "little people" who he "sees" coming out of the magazine rack. I called the Alzheimer's Association and described his behavior. They suggest that he might need to have a psychological evaluation. He was up 27 times last night.

My dad told a neighbor that he and my mother are getting a divorce. This has been an idea he can't let go. He is either convinced that he and my mother are getting a divorce or he believes they are not yet married and he wants to marry her. She has shown him their marriage license but that reassurance doesn't stick with him very long. Once he told my brother, "I'm trying my best to get along with your wife." My brother answered, "She's YOUR wife, Dad."

October 31

Dad fell twice today. Mom didn't allow any children to come to their door for Halloween treats because it would scare Dad. We have been talking to the Geriatric Outreach Psychiatric Facility about admitting Dad. Something has to be done. We can't predict what he will do next.

November 2

Dad was admitted to the hospital for a psychiatric evaluation. They placed him in a room on the second floor of the regular hospital. He is very agitated and we are afraid that he may try to escape through the window and fall the two stories to the sidewalk below. The social services staff person talked with us. I think they believe we are exaggerating. After explaining the situation they advised us to either hire a sitter for the night or have a family member stay with him. My brother stayed. Sometime during the night my dad wanted to get out of bed and use the bathroom. Keith helped him into and out of the bathroom and led him to his bedside. Dad didn't want to get back into bed. He picked up his food tray and swung it at my brother. The nurses came, gave Dad a sedative and placed him in a Gerry chair. It looks like a highchair. He is enraged and jumping it all over the room. I can't believe that they have admitted a person who is in for a psychiatric evaluation to a room on the second floor of the regular hospital. His roommate is a lovely man who is in constant pain and no doubt he is upset by what he is seeing.

November 4

Dad was admitted to the Geriatric Outreach facility. It is a psychiatric facility for older persons with dementia. They will keep him in the facility until medications are able to decrease his behaviors. Dad has been absolutely miserable at home. He was unable to sleep and frightened by his hallucinations. He is out of control with his anger and we have to make this move in order to give him the best possible care. The nurses at the facility say that the average stay is 14 days. It is hard to imagine that Dad will be given anti psychotic medications but that is what it will take to give him relief from the nightmarish state he is in.

November 6

Dad told us that he made a fool of himself because he cried in front of a nurse. We reassured him that he didn't make a fool of himself and that it was okay to cry. I have only seen my dad cry twice in my life, once when his father died and once when his niece passed away. It hurts to see him like this. It is a very nice, quiet facility, not at all as I had imagined. Dad seems to be calmer here with the lack of stimulation.

November 9

Dad came home this morning. It has been two months since his diagnosis. He is very quiet and a bit unsteady on his feet. He is still having some hallucinations but he doesn't seem agitated. I feel like I am his mother. I want to protect him from the things I can't see. He held my hand as we walked to his car. It is like watching dad drift away from the shore and even though we are reaching out to him and trying everything we can think of to keep him with us he drifts farther away every day.

November 16

My brother was up with Dad all night. Dad made 42 trips to the bathroom. He was up putting his street clothes on three times during the night. Even after being awake all night Dad isn't sleepy the next day. He is moving constantly. I don't understand why he is declining so fast. There must be some reason for this.

November 22

During the past month we have learned that my mother-in-law is dying. The congestive heart failure that she has fought for so many years has damaged her beyond repair. Hospice has been helping us through this sorrowful time. Every day my mother-in-law asks how Dad is doing. Every day he asks me how she is doing.

After three days of being by her side she has passed away. I wonder which is the cruelest, to know that the end is coming, as she did or to be inside of a body that has lost all sense of reality. Life is very strange. I almost wish my dad could be released from this hell he is stuck in.

November 24

This evening was the visitation for my mother-in-law. Just as we were about to leave for the funeral home my mother called. Dad couldn't lift his feet up to get out of bed. He was lifeless. I went down the street to check on him and thought he needed to go to the emergency room. As I was leaving for the funeral home the ambulance went past my house, on their way to take my dad to the hospital. I carried a cell phone to the visitation and waited for word from my mom and brother. Finally they called. Dad had been dehydrated. I.V. fluids were given and he was sent home. He felt better immediately. I can't imagine it getting any worse.

December 5

Mother says that Dad is too aware of his situation to be admitted to a nursing home. We don't know what to do. We know that we can't go on like this. It is taking a toll on my mother's health. She is emotionally and physically exhausted. I think that as awful as it is to have to give up I don't see any other choice. We can't go on much longer.

December 11

Today my dad saw a psychiatrist. The doctor gave him some medication, which is usually given in the very early stages of the disease. He held the prescription out in front of my dad's face and said "this will keep him out of the nursing home for at least two years." When my mom and Dad heard that they were so happy. That statement has undone every bit of progress that my mother had made toward accepting Dad's diagnosis. I wish I had been there. How could he be so careless? Hope would be wonderful if it were based on anything real. Dad is so impaired that there isn't anything that will make him better.

December 25

We had our Christmas celebration at my house this year. Dad was very quiet and obviously confused as he watched the grandchildren open presents. I think all the commotion of the holiday made him nervous. Watching him later on a video I could see that it was as if he was on the outside of everything, looking in. It was unbearably sad. He had asked for a new coat for Christmas. When he opened it he didn't react at all. I think he had forgotten wanting one.

January 11

The constant strain of watching dad's every move and trying to keep up with several loads of wet bedding every day are wearing my mom down. She has tried every thing possible to keep him at home.

We have spoken to home health workers but we would need them 24/7. It would be necessary for her to pay someone to be with him around the clock for a duration, which could last for years. Choosing a block of time for a paid sitter wouldn't help because we can't keep up with him the rest of the hours of the day and night. Most of the sitters will not toilet him. They say they are only there to sit by him but not touch him. Dad is very unsteady on his feet and incontinent. He needs to be assisted when he walks.

January 28

Today is my dad's birthday. Earlier today my brother and I took a tour of a nursing home. It looked nice. We hated looking at nursing homes but we have to. We spoke to the marketing staff at length and were convinced that we had found a nice place for him. I gave him pajamas for his birthday. I could feel tears welling up in my eyes as I gave him the gift. He doesn't know that he is leaving in a few days. It is so unreal that my mother and dad, who have been married over 50 years, have five days left to live as man and wife. Could any other illness be so brutal?

January 31

The nurse from the nursing home came to Dad's house today to do an assessment. He was very friendly to her. After she left my mom explained to him that he is going to go to a place where they can take better care of him. He asked where it was and she told him. He asked to go on to bed.

February 3

Dad hasn't mentioned going away to anyone. He hasn't gotten dressed for several days. He stays in his nightclothes and sleeps. He hasn't said a word to anyone since they told him. This is the day that he will leave his home forever. When I walked into the living room he was sitting in his recliner. He looked at me and said, "I hear I'm shipping out." I couldn't believe it. He hadn't said anything about it for days but the minute he saw me he said that. I wanted to undo the whole thing even though I knew there was no other way. He said he didn't want to leave because all of his "friends are here." He meant the family but he no longer realizes who we were. We are his "friends." We have done all we can to keep him at home, failing that we have tried to place him in a good nursing home. The drive there was horrible. It reminded me of being in a funeral procession. He was in the car ahead of me. Keith was driving the car. He told me his heart was breaking but he tried to engage dad in small talk. I followed in my car and I cried all the way there. I had to put a smile on my face when we reached the parking lot of the nursing home. If I had looked sad Dad would have been upset too.

February 5

Visiting the nursing home is far more emotionally draining than I had even imagined. I leave crying every day. I have to hold it inside of me and look like nothing is wrong when I see him or I might scare him. He is so helpless lying in that bed. He used to be such a presence and now he just sleeps. When he talks it is only a whisper. They made him sit in his dining room chair for an hour and a half waiting for lunch. They put a bib on him and he looked like a toddler. He looks so out of place there.

February 8

Dad wouldn't make eye contact today. He wouldn't smile. I wonder what he is thinking. I feel such a sense of guilt. I keep thinking, would he have done this to me?

The guilt that accompanies placing someone in a nursing home can be almost overwhelming. It is very important that the care givers take extra care to guard their health.

March

I leave the nursing home everyday feeling as though I have betrayed him. He is shutting down emotionally. I know inside he has given up. His quality of life is almost zero.

May 15

Dad's call light was being used to tie the curtains back. He was lying across his bed with one leg up in a wheel chair. His clothes were dirty and he hadn't had a shower for a while. He has been hallucinating so much that his roommate asked to be moved to another room. He has the idea his father is dying. He is very upset about it and mentions it repeatedly. His father passed away years ago. Other times he tells us that someone is trying to kill him.

Do not accept less than a high quality of care for your loved one. If, like us you find that you have not selected the best place, don't hesitate to move them. Alzheimer's patients rely upon you to make sure the staff and facility is meeting their needs.

June 12

We have moved Dad to another nursing home. He seems to be thinking clearer there. The activity director keeps him busy. He isn't just lying in a room anymore. He has fallen already. He tried to climb out of the end of his bed.

June 27

Today when I visited my dad it was the saddest sight. He was lying in bed with his hands folded across his chest. He looked waxy and was in a deep sleep. I have never seen a living person look so dead. I feel like I have been to his visitation. I cried all the way home. The decision to place Dad in a nursing home was not something we did lightly. We anguished, we argued, each of us would vacillate from believing that it had to be done to offering up another alternative. With each option we explored there were reasons why they wouldn't work. Problems were mounting hour by hour.

July

Dad has made a good adjustment to this nursing home. They take very good care of him. The nurses baby him and I can see that he enjoys all the attention. He smiles when we come to visit him but there are days when he cannot say our names. There are times when he walks so fast that we can hardly keep up with him and other days when we have to lift him up into a sitting position. It is amazing how he can change so much within an hour. They have him spending his evening hours in a special walker. It has a cloth seat and wheels. He can walk or sit down. The nurses tell us that when he gets overly tired in the evening he tends to pace the halls.

August

Dad has lost ground as far as his ability to communicate. He enjoys getting cards from people and I was very surprised to see that he can still read them. His routine remains the same, sleeping much of the day and eating well at each meal. The nursing home is apparently the only home he remembers. He doesn't even want to go outside. We took him out doors in his wheelchair but he was obviously afraid and wanted to go back inside. He tells us that he has worked all night up on the roof. He says they didn't even give him a break. I guess he thinks he is still a carpenter. Other times he thinks he is back in the Navy. A few days ago he was talking about wanting to join the Boy Scouts. Today he said that he had been elected Vice-President of the United States. He is smiling more than he used to. When he grins he is my "old dad." The confusion doesn't show when he is smiling. It almost hurts to see him smiling at me. I want him to just snap out of this and say "take me out of here."

September

On one of our visits Dad was hiding in his room. He was hiding from the "enemy." We explained to him that the war had been over for a long time, and the Japanese people are our friends. He looked skeptical but accepted the news well. He continues to be restless. He is in and out of bed, looking up and down the halls. I don't know who he is looking for. I am writing in my journal less often because there is little change from day to day aside from his confusion.

October

Dad has had several falls but none of them have done any damage other than skin tears. The falls are inevitable since my dad is in and out of bed constantly and may take off running at any moment. He usually falls after going into a full gallop and trips over someone else's wheelchair.

Even though falls do occur be sure that the nursing home staff is doing all they can to make the nursing home as safe for them as possible.

November

He is well adjusted and except for occasional days when he doesn't make eye contact he seems to be doing fine. I know that he doesn't know who we are but he likes to see us. I think he is having small strokes on those days when he just looks off into space.

December

We went to his Christmas party today. It was so strange to see him there. He still looks out of place at a table with all the other residents. To look at my dad you wouldn't know he had a health problem. He still wears his ball cap. He has the same big grin. Sometimes when I see him standing at the nurse's station he looks like a man checking out of a hotel.

January

Dad had another birthday. What do you give a man who has no idea where he is or who we are. We took him his favorite foods and David gave him a model car. Dad is crazy about it. He told us that he once had a car like that. I don't think that Dad understood it was his birthday but he loved getting the food and the toy car.

February

There have been no major changes. We go and visit and give him lots of hugs and kisses. Dad has always kept his sense of humor and he sometimes "gets it" when you say something funny. He seems content in his room and has never asked to go home. His room is full of photographs of the family, especially his grandchildren and great grand children. He loves all the attention the staff gives him. With his big blue eyes and wide grin they can't resist him. My mother was diagnosed with colon cancer. We couldn't tell him. He would not have understood and he might have thought that HE had cancer. It is very hard to watch my mother go through a life—threatening illness without Dad. After her surgery she should have had her husband by her side. My mother has only her children. She worries about what will become of my dad if she should die. I cannot imagine what it would be like to want to tell my husband that I am sick and afraid and not be able to communicate with him. This truly is a monster of a disease. David, Keith, mom and I are doing all we can to keep him safe and happy.

March

We have been fortunate that aside from Dad's Alzheimer's disease he has remained in good health. His blood sugar is fairly stable and he has not had colds or flu. It is strange that this all seems "normal" now. I didn't think I would ever get use to him living somewhere else. I didn't think I would ever accept this as his fate, but after trying to find some other reason for his symptoms I finally realize that this is reality. I am thankful that he is not in pain or afraid anymore. The worse part was his paranoia. He was like a little boy afraid of the monster under his bed. I hope that doesn't come back. My mother has made a full recovery and she is trying her best to go on with her life. She is neither a widow nor a wife in any real sense of the word. She remains devoted to my father and has taken on the role of his care manager. She will be a part of his life for as long as he lives.

April

Spring is here. The seasons have changed but nothing really changes in my dad's world. He eats, sleeps, walks the hallways and starts the routine all over again the next day. Mom talks about wishing Dad could come home for a visit but we have discussed the fact that it would be a lose/lose situation. If dad recognized his house and his favorite chair and wanted to stay at home we know that he couldn't. If he didn't recognize his home he would be terrified since he has been living in the same room in the nursing home for over a year. We can't put Dad through such an ordeal.

There are days now when my dad can't sit up in his bed without help and days when he can out run the staff. There are days when he stares at us blankly and days when he knows our name. There are days when he is able to walk and many days when every step is a stumble.

The middle stages of Alzheimer's are a roller coaster of emotion for the caregiver. No two days are alike and it is impossible not to feel hopeful when there are moments of clarity.

May

There has been a change in his health. Dad is somewhere between late stage 6 and early stage 7. He is drifting further away from us, except for the occasional moments when his thinking is clearer. Most days his eyes look blank like doll's eyes. His affect is flat. He mumbles when he speaks and what we can understand does not make sense. He is totally dependent for everything except he can still feed himself. His ability to handle utensils is deteriorating. He is not eating all of his meals anymore. Last month he was eating seconds at every meal. I thought that I had given up on the idea that it wasn't Alzheimer's disease and searching for a different explanation. This past week I noticed that his tongue has a scalloped edge and I went in search of a reason for it. I found that a vitamin B-6 deficiency could cause such a thing. I jumped on that idea. Maybe it was something as simple as a vitamin deficiency. Could he be returned to "normal?" I guess I will never stop looking for some other reason why he has lost himself until the day he dies. I hope that isn't ahead for him.

June

We celebrated Father's Day by bringing Dad a muffin. He still loves sweets. The clothes in the nursing home get all mixed so we didn't buy him more clothes. He has more than he can wear. He has a television in his room but he doesn't understand anything that is on. He seems to watch the screen if a cartoon is on. I guess the colors and action attract his attention. I told him "You're a good dad!" And he said, "Well I hope so." He said it in that weak little voice that you can barely hear. After I had been there my brother stopped by. He asked Dad if he had had any company and Dad replied "no."

July

Dad is showing less interest in food. Sometimes he won't open his mouth, even to take a bite of a favorite food. They had started feeding him since he doesn't seem to be able to do it himself. He fell twice the other day. His blood sugar had crashed to 41. The staff has to feed him now and they leave him in his walker at the dining room table. When he first came there he looked out of place, so much more capable than the other residents. Now he is among the worst as far as being able to care for himself. It is getting harder to remember him as he used to be. This is becoming the norm and the dad I use to know is fading. I'm glad that I have videos of him, which were taken before his illness became apparent.

Even before dad was diagnosed I began to experience feelings of guilt. I could see that something was wrong and I wanted to get to the bottom of it. My mother didn't want to see the illness so she made excuses for his mistakes. She and I were at cross purposes as she gave reasons why he was failing and I pushed for a diagnosis. Dad was the oblivious bystander. I felt guilty talking about him behind his back. I felt guilty for enjoying good health when he was falling apart. I felt guilt when I wasn't thinking about him or Alzheimer's disease. Somewhere in my mind I felt like I shouldn't be out enjoying a beautiful day if dad was in a nursing home. I didn't feel right about celebrating holidays at my home, surrounded by family and then going to dad's nursing home to celebrate with him. Guilt is a powerful emotion. Thankfully our rational thoughts were stronger yet.

There are times when I look back over dad's illness and I second-guess every decision that was made. I wonder if we could have done better and then I feel guilty if my answer is "yes". We didn't have the luxury of hindsight and I know we had to learn as we went through it. I wish dad and I had been closer. I loved him but there were so many missed opportunities if only we had known what lie ahead.

Mother tortured herself with the question "What would he have done if it were me with Alzheimer's disease?" She always came up short when she answered that he would never have put her in a home. I don't think that is true at all but I see how she can think those thoughts. She felt she had failed him. We all did. I think dad would have been happy to know that something positive came out of all the misery.

My mind replays moments frozen in time. There is the moment when the psychiatric unit asked dad why he had given me his car keys when I asked him for them. He replied simply "I trust her." That burns into my soul. I know he had to stop driving because he was hallucinating but I have a hard time getting past feeling as though I had betrayed him.

My advice is to do your best to think with your head, not your heart. Your heart will lead you to make decisions that may not be the best for your loved one. Dad was safe and better cared for in the nursing home than he would have been with exhausted frustrated family trying to get through every day and every night. Just know that guilt is a little monster that will try to undermine your confidence and your judgment. Don't let the little monster win.

The Final stage

As summer turned to fall and fall to winter the changes were subtle. He continued to lose weight regardless the amount of food he ate. His appetite never returned. His ability to speak was fading and he communicated in a whisper. We had to lean down and put our ear near his mouth in order to hear him speak. He lost the ability to walk and eventually he could no longer bear his own weight.

For about six months dad had been losing his ability to walk. At first he would have difficulty with his feet seeming to have a life of their own. He would be walking along with someone holding his arm and suddenly his feet would move quickly in place as if he were running in place. The nurse would have him stop and slowly start walking again. He grew weaker by the day. He could not support his own weight and was having to have assistance with every step.

During the month of February dad developed an upper respiratory infection. There was an audible rattle when he breathed. He was hospitalized on March 1st. The respiratory infection had spread through the nursing home and several residents had died. A lung scan indicated a moderate risk that there was a blood clot in one lung and fluid in the other. He was given strong antibiotics and I.V fluids. He was uncomfortable due to a pressure wound on his tailbone. Once he was stable he was transferred back to the nursing home. His stay in the hospital was five days. During that time the antibiotics had rallied him a bit and we had a few days when he would respond to us.

David had won several awards for his radio program and he brought the awards to dad's hospital room. Even though dad had not been very aware of anything going on around him he looked at the awards and said, "That's my Dave." That moment meant so much to my brother. For an instant dad was back.

Once he returned to the nursing home he refused food or water. He would take a few bites or a sip of liquids but meals were a thing of the past. Keith spent every evening trying to get dad to eat something. He would put ice chips in dad's mouth but dad would push them back out. Keith stayed every evening until dad had fallen asleep. Dad's weight had dropped to 103 pounds and he barely made eye contact or tried to speak. He could not roll over in bed, ask a question or even smile. He was like an infant.

Hospice was contacted and they provided him with a special mattress to keep him more comfortable. The mattress inflated and deflated in different areas to relieve the pressure on his skin. Hospice would have been available to service him for several months but as is so often the case they were not called upon until the very end.

In the days before dad's death Dave spoke on air about him. He played songs that were dedicated to him. Dave told the listeners that he would give anything to spend one day with dad, as he had once been, healthy and whole. It was surreal to hear him on my car radio talking about dad as I was on my way to visit him at the nursing home.

I had tried to prepare myself for his death. Two Saturdays in a row we were told that his lungs were filling with fluid and we expected his death. Now that he had stopped taking fluids there was little doubt that it was imminent. How does one prepare for something that we have both prayed for and dreaded? Once again we were filled with a flood of contradictory emotions. You feel guilty for having prayed for an end to their suffering and greedy for wanting to keep them with you for as long as you can.

On March 26th Rose phoned me. She had read my note sent to her by e-mail and she recognized that dad was not far from death. She asked me if I wanted to know what things would signal that the end was near. I told her I did. Rose told me to expect a change in dad's coloring, especially his hands, feet and face. She also said I might see his face appear more gaunt. We left for the nursing home and about an hour into our visit I saw the changes begin. They were subtle and if I hadn't known what to watch for I might not have been there when dad slipped away. I will be forever grateful to Rose for giving me the information that led me to remain by his bedside.

Dad left his Alzheimer's ravaged body without a sound or movement. He simply slipped away. He was surrounded by the love of his family and I know there were unseen angels dispatched to take him home.

When remembering back on the Alzheimer's journey my brother Keith made an observation. He said that dad had become a baby. He needed us for everything. He depended upon us to protect him, to spoon-feed him, to change diapers and to assure him that everything would be alright. The father we had known had faded away so long ago. When the "baby" took its last breath we grieved as we would have grieved a newborn.

Keith had spent so many days holding his hands, talking to him when dad could only stare back. He gave so much to dad in time and in love. David had not only helped to take care of dad he had also made his radio audience more informed about Alzheimer's disease. Mom had never stopped being Jack Glover's wife. She stood by him in the good times and in the bad.

Dad was eulogized as a hard worker, a good provider and a man who loved life. In death he regained the dignity that Alzheimer's disease had stolen. His Navy years were honored with a full military funeral. I know he would have been proud as the men in their uniforms handed mom the folded American flag, played taps and fired off a 21 gun salute. He had made it. He was home.

Through The Looking Glass

*The following is an essay written by an Alzheimer's patient.

Alzheimer's disease is affecting people all over the world. Most books are written to help the caregiver, not the patient. I am a patient, and have been asked to write about what it feels to have this horrible disease.

I am 58-years-old and was diagnosed with early onset Alzheimer's in May 2002.

I lost my husband, my best friend, Tom, in 1992, and decided to relocate to Florida due to severe arthritis.

In 1998, I started misplacing things, but just thought I was a little forgetful and didn't give it any more thought. In 1999, I started having some problems balancing my checkbook, which was unusual for me, as I always balance it to the penny.

In 2000, I had a twelve-hour spinal fusion at the Cleveland Clinic in Ohio, and stayed with my daughter Lisa and family for four months while recovering. My two sons, Jeff and Ken, noticed that I seemed a little confused and forgetful, but we all decided it must be because of the long surgery and severe pain I was in.

When I returned to Florida from Ohio, I told myself I would be fine, just needed to get back to a normal life again.

In February of 2002, I got a disconnect notice from the electric company. I was really angry with the power company. How dare they would make such a mistake with a customer who always paid her bills on time! As I searched for the check number and date in my checkbook, I realized that no check had been sent to the electric company, and the bill was nowhere to be found. I had done a pretty good job until now at hiding my problems. I decided to take a drive one day to a park I visit often on the water. I got half way there, and I couldn't remember how to get the rest of the way. I pulled off to the side of the road, and when I calmed myself down, I turned around and came home. I called a neurologist and made an appointment.

My dear friend and neighbor, Vivian, told me she had noticed a difference in me for quite some time. She noticed that I was forgetting a lot of our conversations, and that she was having to repeat a lot to me.

The standard tests were performed, an MRI of the brain, electroencephalogram (EEG), and a neuropsychological evaluation. The MRI was normal, the EEG was abnormal, showing slow wave activity over both hemispheres. The neuropsychologist called me back in to go over my evaluation. He said he had great concerns about my performance on the test, and everything pointed to early onset Alzheimer's disease. As I stood up to leave, he shook my hand and said, "I'm so sorry." I had come to my appointment by myself because my friend was out of town, and I really believed that I would be told that I was all right and just had a "little memory problem." Driving home all my worst fears I had hidden and tucked away in my head surfaced. The conversations I had with my family and friends that I couldn't remember, not remembering if I had taken my medicine, feeling agitated in a crowd of people, and wanting to get away from them. I remember thinking, "who is going to take care of me when I get worse, how much longer do I have to function independently?" I went to the neurologist a week later and was put on Reminyl to help with the memory. Some days it really seems to help and others it doesn't. I do brain exercises everyday, a lot of reading and crossword puzzles. My spelling has always been excellent, but now I have a dictionary at my side, as I am not always sure how to spell a word.

I am learning that it is okay that I do not remember everything I read or conversations I have with people. At first I felt like I had a sign around me that said "I have Alzheimer's disease." I still get nervous asking a store clerk a question because I know what I want to say, but can't seem to get the words to come out right.

I haven't gotten lost in the car again, but now carry my address book with me and a piece of paper taped on the cover of the book with my address and the address and phone number of my friend. I am less anxious driving now because I have this information with me. I have discovered that most people know the word Alzheimer's, but do not understand it. I have done my homework on this disease, and that makes me feel more in control of my life.

I still live alone with my kitty, Georgia, and plan on remaining independent as long as possible. I have a living will and have discussed it with my children. They understand I don't want to remain on life support if I am terminal.

If I could ask anything of a caregiver it would be:

1. Please be patient with me. It is just as frustrating for me as it is for you trying to answer questions.
2. When at my doctor appointments, don't have a conversation with him/her as though I am not there.
3. Please remember I am still the same person I have always been. I have feelings too, and need to be treated as a whole person.

It is very important that the patient take care of legal matters, future care such as assisted living, nursing home care while we care still able to do this. When the time comes that we can't make our own decisions, this will be a comfort to our loved ones that matters are being handled the way we wanted them to be.

This disease makes a person feel very alone, even though they may be surrounded by loved ones and friends. It is not a disease that shows in the beginning, and I feel like I'm looking through a glass at the other side of the world, a normal world that I am slowly losing touch with. I think the most important thing we as patients need to hang onto is our sense of humor. My family and I have laughed hard at some of the opprobrious situations which will befall us.

Try to get into a support group for patients. They are hard to find, because most are geared to caregivers. If there isn't one and you think you can handle it, start one up.

Above all else, give us as much love, kindness and understanding as you can, even when we aren't aware of it anymore.

Katharine L. Wright

A Map Through the Mist:

Helping You Cope

Accepting the possibility that we or someone we love is entering into the early stags of Alzheimer's disease is a moment when we feel all too human. It is a time when being human and all that it entails become a vivid patchwork of moments that stretch into hours, days, weeks, years, and lifetimes. Stitched in are scraps of memories, hopes, fears, laughter, and tears. Our human frailty glares. In the face of that, our human resilience and strength often reveals themselves in ways that are often surprising and almost always comforting.

Throughout the course of Alzheimer's you will face obstacles. Some will be engendered by the disease and the challenges presented by Alzheimer's and others by personal and family issues. In this section we will address some of the personal and family psychological and practical obstacles that may arise, as well as propose some solutions and coping methods. Practical obstacles caused by the disease itself, as well as those faced by the individual, are found in the subsequent section.

The Obstacles: Setting Reasonable Expectations and Acknowledging Successes

Expectations of Your Abilities

Our strengths at times of stress such as that which follows a diagnosis of a serious health problem often go undervalued and unnoticed. We tend to ignore the myriads of tasks we successfully undertake, both small and large. Failures are often magnified and successes minimized.

Often this common phenomenon plays out in the context of unreasonable expectations. Particularly when Alzheimer's disease is involved, situations can change from moment to moment. Coping has to play out as each new situation arises, setting expectations that one will cope effectively in each situation and thus setting those expectations at unreasonably high levels will inevitably lead to failure. The expectation that you will always succeed is unreasonably high and unattainable. And, if you tend to minimize your successes, you can see how easy it is to end up in a vicious cycle that will leave you feeling like a failure most of the time.

It is very important to keep in mind the simple truth that you are only one person. Your body must have sleep, adequate nutrition, and emotional support. If you believe that you can go it alone throughout the course of your loved one's Alzheimer's illness, you are most likely expecting too much of yourself. The end result may be a deterioration of our own physical health, as well as the idea that you have failed.

As you read the stories of Shirley, Frank and Jack keep in mind the common threads that were challenges for their families. Understand that the illness your loved one suffers from makes keeping them safe an around-the-clock job. Don't expect more from yourself than that which is humanly possible. A team approach is most often required at some point during the course of the illness.

Many people feel that they are the only ones who should care for a family member who has Alzheimer's disease. This is often due to misconceptions about what is expected of a spouse or other family members. It is true that you know the individual with Alzheimer's better than any non-family member could, although outsiders are often adept at seeing things that family members miss because they are *too* close to the individual. But it is generally this understanding of your loved one's likes and dislikes that will improve the quality of his care. It is asking for and accepting help that will enhance your own quality of life and, ultimately, the quality of care your loved one will receive.

Sometimes people expect too little of themselves. Rather than realistically appraising their strengths and weaknesses, they automatically take on an "I can't" attitude. By doing this, they assume defeat even before they have tried. Care giving can be overwhelming at times, and most people will feel "I can't" creeping into their thoughts. There is a difference, though, between occasionally feeling overwhelmed versus assuming before you have tried that care giving is out of the realm of your capabilities. If it is and you are being realistic, good for you—you are aware that you need to find help or alternate living arrangements from the outset. Your realistic appraisal is healthy. If, though, you ignore your own capabilities you are shortchanging both yourself and the person with Alzheimer's disease.

People also sometimes say "I can't cope" regarding the emotional roller coaster that is associated with serious illness in the family. Here again, expectations are set unreasonably low. There is a simple truth here: you do not have a choice. When someone has Alzheimer's, until there is a cure, it is there to stay and it will progress. You have to find ways to cope. Whether it is seeking the services of a professional counselor or finding more informal ways to cope with the emotional upheavals, you must find ways to wend your way through the process.

Expectations of the Person with Alzheimer's Disease

It is equally important not to set expectations too high for the person with Alzheimer's disease. This will not only protect your loved one from needless stress and upset, it will also protect you. Setting your expectations too high will increasingly lead to frustration and anger with your loved one, to disappointment, and to a skewed view of your loved one's functional abilities.

Too often we encounter families who are frustrated with their loved one's behavior and attribute behaviors to obstinacy. Complaints such as, "We lay Mom's clothes out for her and she still won't dress herself," or "Dad is giving up too much and we think he ought to keep driving to maintain his independence" are the kinds of struggles families present.

In order to understand that this is usually not willfulness but is instead, the disease taking effect requires learning more about Alzheimer's itself. The individual who "refuses" to dress most likely does not remember how to dress. He may not even remember what items you laid out or their purpose. An individual who willingly gives up driving may understand better than you how unsafe driving has become due to their impairments. You will need to constantly readjust your expectations of the person with Alzheimer's. The adjustments must often be made on a daily basis and be based on the individual's capabilities on any given day, or even during any given period of time during the day.

Just as it is important not to set your expectations too low for yourself, it is important not to do so for the person with Alzheimer's. In her book *Living in the Labyrinth*, Diana Friel McGowin recounts her experiences living with the relatively early stages of Alzheimer's, including finding that the people around her came to lower their expectations so far that remaining abilities and times when she was accurate were often discounted. She tells a marvelous story about calling her son to ask him to come get rid of the opossum she found in her bathroom, or as she wonderfully writes "evict the 'possum in the privy" (p. 95). By then her family was used to the gaffs Ms. McGowin made and her son Shaun arrived full of sighs and solicitous about his mother's health but clearly certain that this was an Alzheimer's moment.

> I asked wasn't he going to get rid of that 'possum?
> Shaun sighed, then agreed to look into my bathroom.
> After one split second he turned, and in a disbelieving voice whispered to his girlfriend, 'There really is a 'possum in there!" (pp. 95-96)

While your loved one is unlikely to find a "'possum in the privy," avoid the trap of misbelieving everything he says. It becomes all to easy to discount the things that people with Alzheimer's tell us and assume that they are not capable of doing anything. It is important for the psychological well-being of people with Alzheimer's that they not be dismissed out-of-hand. If you expect nothing but inaccuracy in statements made by someone with Alzheimer's disease, you will miss accurate communications. By the same token, assuming affected individuals are incapable of doing anything is demoralizing for Alzheimer's patients and misses opportunities for them to use retained abilities. It is just as important to set realistic expectations for the individual with Alzheimer's disease as it is for yourself.

Expectations of Others

Your expectations of others may be unrealistic. Sometimes expectations are unrealistically high, other times too low. Often the participation of others is up to you. The relationships you have built and maintained with people will frequently be the determining factor in their willingness to help with care giving. Part of your relationships with others is based on how you communicate with the people around you.

Family members and friends helping with care giving is a complex issue. The extent to which family members pitch in is often due to long-standing family variables that remain factors in the family dynamic. Family dynamics are the interplay between individuals in the family that go into creating the normal structure, or system, in the family. It is dynamic because it is a living system and thus ever changing. Families adjust to a structure within their family and people assume different roles that color relationships with other family members. These roles may influence how individual family members are expected to contribute and behave under stressful circumstances.

Roles are tricky things. We are often tacitly labeled and given positions in the family when we are young. Although roles can sometimes be useful when they help provide us with a rough guide to behavior and responsibilities, roles that we assume as children are rarely healthy from a psychological perspective. They limit us and limit the way others view us.

Roles that we have assumed as children are often carried into adulthood. When back among her family of origin, even the most capable and well-rounded adult can be reduced back to an old role that person once played in the family.

Some of the roles that are often found in families, and which may flare when there is a serious illness in the family include:

The family ghost is a person who tends to seclude himself, staying on the edge of the family. When they were children, these children are sometimes considered invisible. As an adult, the individual may come in and out of their parents' lives and may continue this practice when one parent is diagnosed with Alzheimer's.

The family hero or rescuer is a child who will try to keep peace in the family. This child will do all he or she can to be a "good girl" or "good boy." When a serious illness enters the family, the hero as an adult may continue his ways and step in to take on a significant amount of responsibility. The danger is relying too heavily on this individual—rescuers often end up being resentful of the burdens that are placed on them.

The family clown will use humor or theatrics to draw attention to herself. As an adult, this individual may be drawn to a profession that draws a spotlight. The clown is often also a rescuer: she lightens tensions and can draw attention away from problematic situations. As an adult in a family with Alzheimer's, these characteristics may reemerge and be useful when it comes to relieving tension. The danger comes when an individual is not sensitive to drawing the spotlight too much and relies on her "clown" tendencies to the exclusion of listening and adjusting behavior appropriately. And it is easy to miss any underlying distress the "clown" may be experiencing, thus leaving the person isolated with her feelings.

The scapegoat is a family member upon whom blame will fall. This person will be held responsible for most misfortunes or family problems. The scapegoat can never win; he may be the hero for a day but will soon be the target of blame again. When the scapegoat is the person who becomes ill or dies, the burden of that position will often shift onto another family member.

The problem child is a family member who receives focus because of his or her problems. Often this family member is *not* the problem in a family, but rather reflects family pathologies. Rather than address the problem with the family system, though, families tend to focus on one family member as "the" problem. Many families dismiss attempts by this person to help and, instead, may continue to consider that individual too problem-ridden to make any meaningful contribution.

Each of these roles, and others limit the way we view people as children and later as adults. When Alzheimer's enters the family, the roles may be used to limit family member participation.

Expectations: Coping and Solutions:

Personal Expectations and Acknowledging Successes

Learn to acknowledge your successes, even if is only a silently celebrated sense of accomplishment. It is imperative to remember that you are, indeed, human and when faced with caring for a family member with Alzheimer's disease, it is a process through which you will have both successes and failures. You will make mistakes. Your mistakes will rarely, if ever, be of any significant proportion. You will have successes. Just as important as it is to learn from our mistakes, it is important to learn from the successes. Do not be afraid to be human throughout the process.

Know your limitations. Knowing your weaknesses and limits is a tremendous strength. But knowing your limitations if you are unwilling to ask for help is an exercise in futility. If you know your limitations but constantly disavow their impact on care giving or your own well-being as a caregiver, you are likely to compromise both your own well-being and that of the person with Alzheimer's disease. Challenge yourself to tackle things you think you cannot do, but learn to know when you are pushing too far and you and your care giving will suffer as a result.

At the same time, know your strengths. If you are prone to expecting failure before you begin, you will experience failure. It is just as important to acknowledge your strengths as it is your weaknesses, and to capitalize on your strengths and compensate for your weaknesses.

One of the toughest challenges you will face is assessing your situation realistically and adjusting your expectations accordingly. The expectation that you will be able to care for the person with Alzheimer's disease by yourself throughout the course of his or her illness may or may not be realistic for you. It is unrealistic for most people. This does not mean that nursing facilities are the only options. You do have options, but you must be willing to avail yourself of them. If you doggedly adhere to your elevated expectations despite evidence that they are unrealistic and not working, you are damaging both yourself and your loved one who has Alzheimer's.

Try to understand where your unrealistic expectations spring from. Perhaps you know someone who was able to independently care for a person with Alzheimer's disease and you believe you should be able to do the same. This is a mistake. No two individuals, or their situations are the same. You did not live in the house with that person—there may have been problems with care giving that you are not aware of and the person is not telling you about.

You may expect that it is your duty as a spouse or responsible family member to shoulder the responsibility on your own. Again, this is a mistake. Part of being a responsible and loving family member is to do what is best for everyone involved, and that includes both you and the person with Alzheimer's. Often, caring for this person on your own will not be the best for either of you. Caregiver burnout is common and it will affect your well-being, as well as that of your loved one. It is much easier to avoid burnout when you have assessed your situation realistically, thrown the phrases "I should be . . . " or "I should do . . . " out the window, and set a realistic standard for yourself and the people around you.

If you find yourself caught up in a cycle where you feel as if you have nothing but failures, you need to find ways to break out of that cycle. Talk to friends and family members who may be able to help you engage in a reality check, including helping you to see your successes and adjust your expectations. People who have dealt with Alzheimer's in their own family may be particularly helpful. Support groups may also be an invaluable resource at these times— either online support groups or one available in your community. People who have filled shoes similar to yours have often felt the same emotions and can help you achieve a greater balance in how you view your situation.

If you have faced reality and are in a situation where failure is unavoidable, based on the circumstances, reevaluate the whole environment and the circumstances that are continually causing problems. Take a realistic look at things that you can change and what needs to be done to affect changes. This may require making difficult decisions and enlisting the help of others to help you make changes, but it may be necessary. If you are, evaluating accumulating problems realistically, the aggregation of difficulties may be an indication that significant changes are in order.

Expectations of the Person with Alzheimer's Disease

It is essential to educate yourself about Alzheimer's disease. Read the chapters in this book that provide information about Alzheimer's behaviors, problems that often arise during the course of the disease, and what happens to the brain afflicted with Alzheimer's disease. Read, also, about solutions to frequently encountered problems.

It is important to encourage the individual with Alzheimer's to independently undertake tasks they are able to, help with those that require assistance, and learn to recognize when you must step in and do things for the person with Alzheimer's. This may take time and some trial and error and it will change over time. If, however, your expectations do not change, you will find the individual increasingly unable to meet those demands. Make flexibility your rule.

No one wants to appear incompetent and, particularly early in the course of the disease, people cover up their deficits. While it preserves dignity, it also leads people to expect more of the person with Alzheimer's than he or she may be able to handle. Abilities also fluctuate, sometimes from minute to minute. This may be due to a number of factors, including brain damage that is only partial and allows sporadic transmission of information. In addition, skills in various areas of functioning will be impaired or preserved to different degrees—an ability to tackle one task successfully does not mean that a task that requires slightly different skills can be accomplished. You will learn through trial and error, careful observation, and Alzheimer's disease education, what your family member can accomplish safely and independently.

Overwhelmingly the behavior problems that arise during the course of Alzheimer's disease are due to the effects of the disease and the brain damage it causes. This is not to say, though, that a person's characteristics are erased when they have Alzheimer's. For example, stubbornness in an individual who is characteristically stubborn may persist. Early in the course of the disease, some behavior problems may be due to her preexisting stubbornness, to psychological factors, or may be compounded by new disease variables. Even early in the course of the disease, she will be far less able to guide and choose her behaviors than she was prior to the onset of Alzheimer's, so you must always take the disease variable into account even very early in the disease. You will need to learn how to tell the difference between willfulness and behaviors that are more rooted in the disease. Although it is next to impossible to be right all of the time when forced to make these distinctions, it will help both you and the person with Alzheimer's if you are as sensitive as possible to the differences between disease-based problems and the individual's own characteristics. In the early stages of the disease, the problems that arise may be due to more of a mixture of the person's preexisting personality and the disease process. As the disease progresses, it is increasingly the disease that is causing problems, and during the middle and later stages, it is essentially entirely Alzheimer's that causes the behaviors and psychopathologies that are so problematic.

Keep treating the person with Alzheimer's in a respectful and loving way. This may seem axiomatic, but it is all too easy to talk down to a person with Alzheimer's disease. Being treated with respect and dignity is as important to someone with Alzheimer's as it is to anyone else, perhaps more as the disease begins to rob them of abilities. Too often people with Alzheimer's are treated in infantile ways and it is demoralizing. Your expectations must constantly be adjusted and at times the person's behavior will be reduced to childlike levels, particularly as the disease progresses. You will need to find a balance between empowering the person with Alzheimer's, treating him or her with respect and dignity, and still guiding and caring for that person in ways that are similar to how you might care for a young child. Throughout the disease, think about how you would like to be treated if you were you in their position. Always treat them, as you would want to be treated.

Expectations of Others

You may believe that your friends and family will be involved in your loved one's care and in many cases they will be. Here, too, you will fare best if you throw your "should" thoughts out the window—people often do not behave as we think they "should," and expecting people to participate in care in ways we think they "should" often leads to disappointment and anger.

As early as can be managed in your loved one's illness, it is important to put plans in place that detail what role others will play in your loved one's care. If possible, hold a family meeting to outline how each family member will contribute, the limitations to the contributions individual family members can or will make, and how to capitalize on individual strengths most effectively. Be flexible as needs may change over time. It is imperative that you tell people specific things they can do to help you when help is offered. The offer may not be repeated as time goes on.

If you are the spouse of an Alzheimer's patient, you will find the jobs that were filled by your spouse now fall on your shoulders. Regardless of how busy you become your grass will grow, gutters will clog, dust will fall, and finances will need to be handled. Seemingly unimportant little things can become major stressors if you have no one to help you.

If you are the adult child of a person with Alzheimer's, your roles will also shift. You may be asked to undertake personal and practical care tasks that are uncomfortable, and you will often find yourself in a parental role as the person's ability to do things independently diminishes. This all occurs in the context of adult children leading their own complicated and busy lives, sometimes leaving them feeling overwhelmed.

Plan ahead for the time you will need to take care of the jobs that have been shifted from your spouse's or parent's shoulders to yours, and for the tasks that you generally undertake yourself but which are now coupled with care giving. Take time early in the course of the disease to investigate services available to the person with Alzheimer's and the family. Talking to other families that have experienced Alzheimer's in the family, or finding information through libraries and the Internet, may help you to anticipate problems you had not considered. The more you know about available services and financial assistance, the less you will be thrown for a loop by the un-anticipated.

The hardest task may be to redefine how you view family members. Families tend to work as systems, and the roles that many families use to conceptualize each person's place in the family help to organize the system in peoples' minds. Note that these roles are often tacit; many of you may be saying to yourself, "Our family doesn't do that. We view each person as an individual." That may or may not be true of your family. Take the time to look as objectively as possible at your family to analyze if people have been pigeonholed into certain roles.

The family will operate most effectively if each person is allowed to contribute based on his or her strengths, and is allowed to contribute in ways that you may not expect. Try to see your family members as you may never have seen them before—see the possibilities and the strengths in the person, regardless of how you may have thought about that individual in the past. Not all family members will be able to contribute significant help during this process, but do not make the mistake of counting people out prematurely.

Being flexible throughout the process will help you deal more effectively with the variety of issues that will arise. Changes that occur throughout the course of the disease will require continual decision-making and changes in family structure. Adult children will have to make decisions for a parent, thus altering the traditional parent-child roles. Some siblings may be called on or may assume more active roles in caregiving and decision-making than others. If your family is excessively rigid when it comes to shifting roles and responsibilities, it may help to seek brief professional assistance at various points along the way. Even one family meeting with a mental health professional or a combination of involved professionals may help to sort through and solve temporary practical and emotional roadblocks.

Some individuals and families are better than others at being flexible. If it is not one of your strengths, do your best to work it into the fabric of your life. Alzheimer's is a disease that requires flexibility. Some families accept outside help more easily than others. Pride, shame, stubbornness, and a host of other variables that cause people to shut others out will cause needless additional difficulty with coping with any extended illness. Accepting and even soliciting outside assistance is wise, healthy, and advisable, not a sign of weakness or failure.

Family members may also differ regarding abilities to cope with practical needs. Again, this is normal and expected. Try to capitalize on individual strengths and, where possible, divide care giving responsibilities based on these individual strengths and weaknesses. Accusations regarding the relative contributions, or lack of contributions, of each person are destructive and likely to make family members less willing to actively participate in family responsibilities. When some family members feel overburdened, try holding a family meeting and discussing how each family member can be of assistance. Attacking family members you feel are not doing their part will most likely push those individuals into defensive positions and decrease their willingness to participate. Helping them to see how their unique strengths may be used to help with the practical needs engendered by Alzheimer's disease is likely to encourage cooperation.

Finally, each member of the family should try to live their lives as normally as possible. Expecting family members to stop living their lives when Alzheimer's creeps into the family is unreasonable and unhealthy. Certainly, adjustments have to be made, but they should not be so drastic that your life comes to a halt.

Clearly, if there is one family member who assumes the role of a primary caregiver for a loved one who remains at home, that individual is likely to have to alter his lifestyle significantly. In such a case, that individual needs help and respite. Even finding time to take a bath can become problematic when a person with Alzheimer's disease is active and tends to wander. Setting up a schedule for respite will prevent the primary caregiver from having to ask for that needed assistance—all too often, caregivers will not ask. If family members cannot participate, try to hire a caregiver for even brief amounts of time during the week. If financial considerations make this impossible, think creatively and reach out for help. Enlist the help of neighbors, church members, volunteer community groups, and others in your community who may be able to provide assistance. All family members, including the family member with Alzheimer's disease, will benefit from it. The more family members can maintain their physical and psychological health, the better all members of your family will fare.

Do not assume that any given family member will or should assume primary care giving roles. Each family member has her own set of personal obligations and needs and those should be taken into consideration. Spouses of persons with Alzheimer's disease are usually elderly themselves and should not be expected to undertake the care giving role without assistance. Too often undertaking this role without sufficient assistance results in declining health in formerly healthy spouses. Research has even linked it to increased mortality rates among elderly caregivers who report increased mental or emotional stress (Schulz & Beach, 1999).

Hinting versus Asking

How do you react when someone asks a favor of you. Do you feel resentful? Do you automatically feel used? Probably not. How do you feel when someone hints that they need something? Hinting may feel more comfortable for you but for the person on the receiving end it is not comfortable. Hinting requires the other person to interpret your vague and veiled request, make assumptions about your communication, and offer help based on those assumptions. You are asking the impossible—you are asking people to read your mind and to correctly guess at all times what you really need. With an open mind please imagine the following dialogue.

Caregiver: Are you going to the store today?
Friend: I hadn't planned to go today but I can if you need something.
Caregiver: No, there isn't anything I have to have.
Friend: I don't mind going. What do you need?
Caregiver: No, don't make a special trip. I'll get by.

This conversation can go on forever and it serves to make the person on the receiving end feel like he is failing you and he becomes frustrated with trying to pull information out of you. JUST ASK. If you use this hinting style of dialogue you will drive people away. It leaves people feeling inadequate, manipulated, and ultimately angry. If you need something be direct and pleasant about it. People tend to respond to this in a positive way.

One of the truths most of us have found is that people want to help. It feels good to feel needed and useful. Particularly when a family member is seriously ill, the wish to be able to "fix it" fills most people. But we know we can't "fix it." What we can do is help in any way we can. It is up to each family member to set his or her limits and be willing to say "no" when feeling overtaxed or when they must attend to other aspects of their lives instead of undertaking a care giving task. Families who work as teams are far less likely to find themselves in a position where any individual feels overtaxed for any extended period of time. When care giving is shared the responsibility tends to be spread out enough that no individual feels overburdened. For those families where sufficient help is not available or cooperative care giving within the family is not working, ask friends and local volunteers to help and avail of yourself of local community services.

All too often we push help away because we are too proud or stubborn or even embarrassed to admit that we cannot do it all. It isn't a sign of weakness to accept assistance. When Alzheimer's is involved, it is a virtual necessity.

Deborah Recalls Her Experiences with Expectations

I found myself getting very frustrated when Dad was diagnosed with Alzheimer's. I was of the belief that there is always an answer if you just look hard enough. I expected myself to be able to "fix" what was going wrong inside of him by researching the disease. When that didn't work I expected to be able to help my mother to the point that dad could stay at home for the duration. As you have read in my section of the book Dad was getting up constantly through the night and trying to wander during the day. My mother, brothers and I were all trying to keep up, but Dad seemed to run on empty. Once again I felt I had failed. We all felt we had failed Dad and ourselves.

My mother set expectations of "what would he have done if it were me?" She would always answer this question with a statement like "He wouldn't have put me in a nursing home." No one can measure up to the "what ifs". She was measuring her actions against those things she imagined he would have done. We all tend to overestimate what someone else is capable of. In hindsight I would say, "Do the best that you can do." If you have done that then you can ask no more of yourself.

My mother expected a great deal from my father. Her belief that he could remember things if he would try harder was frustrating to both of them. She had him recite nursery rhymes trying to help him to keep his memory. Her expectations were not realistic and when the memory practice didn't work she was broken hearted and Dad was embarrassed. Just as I had set the expectation of finding a cure for Dad, Mom had set an expectation of holding the disease at bay. Neither of us could meet our expectations and the result was a flood of guilt, anger and a sense of failure. Looking back I am comforted by the fact that we all did the best that we could for Dad.

The Obstacles: Guilt and Anger

There is plenty of fodder for anger when someone we love has Alzheimer's: anger at Alzheimer's attacking someone you love; anger at God for allowing it to happen; anger at daily stresses caused by the situation; anger at institutionalized systems that add practical and emotional stresses; anger at family members and friends who you perceive aren't being helpful; anger that life didn't work out as expected; anger at people who have healthy spouses and parents; anger that the demented person is no longer able to provide the companionship and protection they once did; anger that the remaining spouse will be left alone; anger at the cruelty of Alzheimer's; anger that life plans have to be altered for any number of people, and so many more. You will have your own list of big and small issues that provoke feelings of anger, and your triggers will be different from those of other people.

Reasonable levels of anger are normal and are an expected part of the process. We say reasonable because anger can range from mild irritation to rage, the latter being an unreasonable and unhealthy reaction. All family members will experience reasonable levels of anger at various times during the process. We all become frustrated and angry at times. It is amazing that we expect that aspect of human nature to change during the most stressful times of our lives. Do not expect yourself to shelve your normal human emotions when someone you love has Alzheimer's. Behaviors caused by Alzheimer's disease are often frustrating and often provoke feelings of anger.

Many will feel guilty when they become angry, particularly when they are angry at the person with Alzheimer's disease. Like anger, different issues will provoke guilt for different people. When it comes to Alzheimer's disease, many different factors can provoke guilt: becoming angry at the person with Alzheimer's; choosing to move a family member to a nursing facility; choices that you must make along the course of the disease; feeling that something one has done or not done has contributed to a fall or other problem; responding to the person with Alzheimer's ineffectively; guilt over anger at other family members.

Anger internalized may lead to lashing out, substance abuse, depression, physical ailments, and a host of other problems. When we are angry with a person or event but do not recognize it as such, we also tend to displace anger. Displacement means that we experience and display anger about all kinds of things, except the things about which we really are angry. Holding anger at one's boss inside and then taking the anger out on family members is an example of displacement. Being angry because your loved one has Alzheimer's disease but failing to recognize or cope effectively with that anger and, instead, lashing out at the person with the illness and other people is another example.

Anger often masks other emotions. Fear, sadness, and guilt are three emotions that can hide in the shadows of anger. Anger, although often unpleasant, is an easier emotion for many people to recognize and accept than emotions like fear, sadness, and guilt. Sadness, for example, is an emotion that we often try to avoid and disavow. Particularly in societies where crying and other exhibitions of sadness are discouraged, anger is often the emotion that displaces the sadness we really feel.

Sometimes, however anger is just anger. Knowing the difference between the times that you are using anger to cover other emotions and when anger is just what it seems means learning about yourself and being open to continued learning and growth.

Guilt is not an entirely useless emotion—it helps us to self-monitor and provides us with feedback regarding how we think we are measuring up to our personal standards. Our standards, though, often take us back to the old expectations theme—if our expectations are unrealistic, we will provide ourselves with unrealistic feedback and feel needlessly guilty. Guilt is useless and destructive. People often feel guilty over situations over which they have no control and for irrational reasons. The desire to please other people, for instance, is an example of guilt that can provide you with irrational feedback—you cannot please everyone all of the time. Feeling guilty over the times that you feel you have not pleased everyone is irrational and a waste of your precious time and energy. Like anger, guilt can accumulate and turn inwards so that you berate yourself for every infinitesimal slip below standards, standards that we remind you may be unreasonably high. They certainly are unreasonable if you expect that you will never make a mistake about which you may then feel guilty!

Anger and Guilt: Coping and Solutions

First, acknowledge that you will occasionally become angry. You may think it is irrational to become angry at a disease or even at a person for developing a disease, but it is one of many normal responses when someone we love is diagnosed with a serious illness. Emotions often aren't rational, they just are. What is important is what we do with the emotions—how you handle your emotions is important to your well-being and that of the person with Alzheimer's disease.

Learn to take time for yourself to puzzle through the emotions you are experiencing. We all have strengths and weaknesses, and understanding our emotions is no exception: some people are more experienced and better at it than others. Just because it is unfamiliar territory does not mean that you are not capable of this kind of inner exploration, it just means that you frequently have not used a skill you most likely have. Understanding the source of our emotional reactions is an important step in dealing with them effectively.

As we have noted before, anger is often mixed with sadness, even if we don't recognize the mix. Allow yourself time and the leeway to experience the anger and explore the thoughts associated with it. If it is masking a sadness, let the sadness come through. You will be amazed at the degree to which your anger is usually diminished if you deal with any underlying grief.

Everyone occasionally experiences anger and a brief flash of tempered anger is not generally a serious event. When one has a family member with Alzheimer's disease, though, one must guard against letting your anger accumulate and against expressing your anger around the individual with the disease. We have learned that expressing emotions is healthy, and this is often true. One exception is expressing anger around someone with Alzheimer's. People with Alzheimer's disease have difficulty handling other peoples' strong emotions so caregivers must learn to express them elsewhere. This is particularly true of anger and frustration.

When you become frustrated and angry with the person who has Alzheimer's, there can be a number of reasons. Make sure you aren't displacing anger—are you angry about something other than the event that provoked your anger? If so, recognize it and deal with the source of your anger. Do what is necessary to cope with and dispel the underlying anger.

If it is a specific event associated with the individual who has Alzheimer's that has triggered your anger, take a step back, take a deep breath, and try to address the individual calmly and effectively. Becoming angry with them will only make people with Alzheimer's anxious and make the situation worse.

Try to put yourself in the shoes of the person with Alzheimer's. Read the section in this book on the reactions of people who have been diagnosed with Alzheimer's as well as books written by people diagnosed with the disease. Remember that more often than not it is the disease causing your loved one's behavior, and as the disease progresses to later stages it is almost entirely the disease.

If your anger is out of proportion and you find yourself blowing up, or if you find that you are frequently angry, it is time to take a care giving break and to get help. Explosive, omnipresent anger is a sign for caregivers that they are burned out and need help. Help is available, but you must be willing to ask for it and accept it when it is offered. Getting personal help means talking to people who you feel will be the most help to you: a good friend, other family members, your pastor, a professional counselor, and support group members are just some resources.

Anger can be induced and sustained by irrational thinking. Below are some types of irrational thinking and suggested counter-thoughts. Note that there are other causes and you should apply your own examples, as well as use suggested counter-thoughts as a template to apply to your own brand of irrational thinking.

1) Shoulds. We often think things *should* be different than they are and that people *should* behave in certain ways. Our wishes and beliefs are essentially translated into more concrete demands about how the world should work. Our "should" thoughts are directed at others and at ourselves and often lead to frustration and anger that the world, and even yourself, do not behave in ways that you think *should* happen.

   1   Counter-thoughts: People and the world are just not going to operate in ways we think they *should*. Remind yourself that your frustration, disappointment, desires, and other variables are driving your "should" thoughts. Change what you reasonably can and learn to let go of the rest.

2) Exaggerated or extreme thinking. "I really upset Dad when I let him see me so frustrated this morning. I just can't do

this, it's too hard and I'm no good at it." In this example, the event moves from being an opportunity for learning how to handle situations when you are a caregiver to a self-defeating statement. The event is exaggerated beyond a single event to a prediction of total failure in all future events.

- Counter-thought: "Well, I goofed on that one but it's not the end of the world. What can I learn from this goof and do differently next time?"

3) Overgeneralizing. This is often indicated by the use of the words always, never, and everything. "Everything I do ends up being a flop," is one example. Although there are instances when the use of these words is accurate, they often indicate that you are overgeneralizing and thinking irrationally.

1 Counter-thoughts: Call yourself on it when you find yourself overgeneralizing. Have you really *never* succeeded at *anything?* That is impossible! We sometimes look at large failures and overlook our daily small successes. When you catch yourself using any of these blanket terms, realize that you are most likely overgeneralizing and excluding myriads of instances that counteract your generalization.

4) Blaming. In this instance, we are referring to blaming others for your behavior and your feelings. No one *makes* you behave or feel as you do. You are in charge of your own behavior and your own feelings.

2 Counter-thoughts: Realize that you and you alone are responsible for your thoughts, feelings, and behaviors. Blaming in general only leads to anger and hurtfully diminishing the people you blame. It may make you

feel better temporarily if you lead yourself to believe others are to blame for your bad feelings or behavior, but it is ultimately self-destructive.

5) Arriving at irrational conclusions and making blanket statements. "I talk and talk but no one will ever understand me." Some of this may be do to the nature of the way that you communicate and some may be due to your choice of listeners. Regardless of the cause, a blanket statement is irrational.

> 3 Counter-thought: In this particular instance, trying to communicate your thoughts and feelings in different ways may improve others' ability to understand you. And, while there will certainly be people who do not understand what you are going through, there will be people who do. When you need that understanding, seek out people who are more likely to listen well, understand you, help you express yourself when you are not clearly communicating your feelings, and leave you feeling that you have been understood and appreciated.

6) Negative self-statements. "I'm not smart enough to understand all of this stuff about Alzheimer's so I'll never be a good caregiver." You may be able to come up with many of your own statements that you use that put yourself down.

> 4 Counter-thought: I may not understand everything about Alzheimer's and the brain, but I get enou8gh to do a good job as a caregiver. And what I don't understand I can learn if I need to.

Stress accumulates and can lead to feeling angry. There are many ways you can find to relieve stress that leads to anger. The topic of stress and stress relief is covered more fully under "Caregiver Stress." Stress relieving techniques can help to dispel your anger which, when there is a serious illness involved, is often caused by accumulations of stress. Whether you find sports or reading a good book or going out to dinner a stress reliever, you must find ways to engage in those things that decrease the amount of stress you are experiencing. If you are unable to do anything to relieve your stress because of the demands on your time, then find ways to decrease those demands. If it means accepting help from others, accept it.

When you find yourself becoming angry and frustrated more than normal, it is a good time to take a stress-relieving break. Remember, you are normal and human. These are human reactions. How you handle your emotions, though, is important to your well-being and that of the person with Alzheimer's disease. If you find yourself directing your anger and frustration at your affected loved one, learn from the mistake and remind yourself to find other outlets for your stress.

Remember that your loved one will have good and bad hours. Planning for good and bad days will leave you unprepared for the shift that can occur from hour to hour. Being prepared and forewarned will help you to expect the unexpected, and will leave you less upset when the unexpected occurs.

Frequent or unremitting anger drives people away. At a time in your life when you need people most, you will drive them away. If you cannot open up and tend to the anger you will find yourself completely alone. Your friends and family will eventually avoid the bitterness that you exude. So find ways to dispel your anger. Mental health professionals and support groups may be particularly good resources if your anger has settled in and even escalated.

Finally, anger and bitterness about your loved one's Alzheimer's disease can merge and almost take on a life of it's own if allowed to do so. People who find themselves filled with almost omnipresent anger and bitterness have to realize that it is a choice: you have chosen to let those feelings take up residence and pervade your life. You can choose to rid yourself of this pervasive and destructive mindset or choose to hold onto it. The only person who is hurt by holding onto anger and bitterness is the person in whom it resides and smolders.

When you feel guilty, use your guilt to learn. If there are things that you recognize and can change that have led to your guilt, work on making those changes. If your guilt is irrational, address the underlying irrational beliefs that lead to irrational guilt. Challenge those beliefs and you will find your guilt dissipating.

Deborah Recalls Her Experiences with Anger and Guilt

Anger swings a sword at everyone within an arms length. You hurt so badly but crying won't touch it. Anger narrows your eyes to slits and tightens your chest and cheats you out of days that you could have spent holding their hand and reliving the good old days. It will eat you alive if you let it.

"It's not fair!" I remember saying that so many times as a child. Alzheimer's isn't fair and I hate it more than anything else and I am angry that it is a part of our world. I am angry that it sneaked up on my dad and stole his smile and replaced it with a fog. I am so angry that I won't let myself be angry any more. It has taken all I will allow.

It "anger" brought out the worst in some who should have been at their most gentle. They wielded the sword and held everyone back, those who would have hugged them. It was a part of the monster that caused the most upset, chaos and turmoil. It is the monster I most resent, the way it splits up those who should be a unit and lays wide open old wounds. What anger took will not return. The words can't be unspoken. It won.

We have come out the other end of the fog with hurt feelings, misgivings, resentment and wasted days. Learn from us. Don't speak before thinking. Pain cannot be measured and to assume you hurt worse than others is a selfish and mean thing to say.

Even before Dad was diagnosed I began to experience feelings of guilt. I could see that something was wrong and I wanted to get to the bottom of it. My mother didn't want to see the illness so she made excuses for his mistakes. She and I were at cross purposes as she gave reasons why he was failing and I pushed for a diagnosis. Dad was the oblivious bystander. I felt guilty talking about him behind his back. I felt guilty for feeling good when he was falling apart. I felt guilt when I wasn't thinking about him or Alzheimer's disease.

Somewhere in my mind I felt like I shouldn't be out enjoying a beautiful day if Dad was in a nursing home. I didn't feel right about celebrating holidays at my home, surrounded by family and then going to Dad's nursing home to celebrate with him. Several times, we as a family were tempted to bring dad home to celebrate a holiday but we knew it was a tough situation. If Dad recognize his real home and wanted to stay it would be so heartbreaking to have to take him back. If he didn't know where he was he would be afraid. Guilt was powerful. Thankfully our rational thoughts were stronger yet.

There are times when I look back over Dad's illness and I second guess every decision that was made. I wonder if we could have done better and then I feel guilty if my answer is "yes". We didn't have the luxury of hindsight and I know we had to learn as we went through it. I feel guilty when I wish Dad and I had been closer. I know I loved him but there were so many missed opportunities if only we had known what lay ahead.

My mother tortured herself with the question "What would he have done if it were me with Alzheimer's disease?" She always came up short when she answered that he would never have put her in a home. I don't think that is true at all but I see how she can think those thoughts. She felt she had failed him. We all did.

I feel guilty writing this book because I don't want to do anything to deepen the pain that the disease has wrought. My heart breaks as I relive all of the pain but I know that the things we have lived will help others do better. I think Dad would have been happy to know that something positive came out of all the misery.

My mind replays moments frozen in time. There is the moment when the psychiatric unit asked Dad why he had given me his car keys when I asked him for them. He replied simply "I trust her." That burns into my soul. I know he had to stop driving because he was hallucinating but I have a hard time getting past feeling as though I had betrayed him.

My advice is to do your best to think with your head, not your heart. Your heart will lead you to make decisions that may not be the best for your loved one. Dad was safe and better cared for in the nursing home than he would have been with an exhausted and frustrated family trying to get through every day and every night. Just know that guilt is a little monster that will try to undermine your confidence and your judgement. Don't let the little monster win.

FAMILY MEMBER PSYCHOLOGICAL REACTIONS TO SYMPTOMS AND DIAGNOSIS

The Obstacles: Denial

Acknowledging a problem exists is a first step in the process of coping with Alzheimer's, one that is often a battle between what our intellects see and what our hearts want to believe. The individual who is diagnosed with Alzheimer's disease may or may not have been aware of the early symptoms. Lack of awareness may be due to denial, cognitive impairment, or a combination of the two. Individual family members are also likely to experience varying degrees of awareness. When families are separated geographically, family members who speak occasionally with the individual who has been diagnosed with Alzheimer's may challenge the diagnosis. "After all, Mom sounds fine when I talk to her on the phone . . . I think people are overreacting and she's been misdiagnosed." Sometimes it is the people who live with someone in the early stages of Alzheimer's who may not notice changes until they are glaring, or until others point out a problem. Symptoms may be minimized or explained away in a variety of ways. Diagnoses may be challenged even when there is incontrovertible evidence to support the diagnosis.

The term "denial" is overused these days and has come to take on completely negative connotations. It is, however, a real and common psychological defense in reaction to emotional turmoil. Just as denial can be harmful, it can also be a helpful defense. We use it unconsciously and automatically because it is protective, it temporarily helps us to traverse perilous psychological territory. When someone we love is diagnosed with any kind of serious illness, denial may give people precious time to marshal psychological resources needed to face serious situations.

One factor that makes denial such a common defense when facing Alzheimer's disease in the family is the nature of the disease. Alzheimer's disease is stealthy. We expect to see some cognitive changes as people age and, unless one knows what is normal versus abnormal, many people dismiss early stages as part of the normal aging process. But the cognitive and behavioral changes found in Alzheimer's disease are anything but normal. In fact, few striking or significant changes are seen during the course of normal aging. Cognitive processing may be a little slower, there are relatively mild memory changes in some limited aspects of the memory process, and there are other relatively subtle changes. When the changes are striking and begin to interfere with daily functioning, it indicates a more serious process is taking place.

Denial: Some Solutions and Coping

Denial only becomes problematic when it interferes with obtaining necessary care, taking care of practical issues, avoiding seeking a diagnosis, or when it is used excessively over long periods of time. We emphasize here that when it interferes with obtaining necessary medical attention, when it sets the stage for the individual with Alzheimer's to engage in dangerous activities, and when it prevents you from listening to the concerns of the person with Alzheimer's, it becomes a serious problem that must be confronted.

Continued denial may cause injury to the person with Alzheimer's, an unacceptable consequence of denying that there is a problem.

There are times, though that it is less urgent to confront denial. Although it may cause friction within families when individual family members are in different phases of coping with the onset of the illness and the diagnosis, as well as when the disease progresses in later stages, understanding its functions may help you to tolerate and empathize with the different ways that we come to terms with the diagnosis and progression of the disease.

First, recognize that denial rarely lasts over long periods of time. It may ebb over time and reappear for brief periods during the course of your loved one's illness. In situations that do not require immediate action, even brief amounts of time may give the person in denial necessary space to take in the reality on her own terms. Once people have been able to find some equilibrium, accepting reality becomes easier and will occur. Family members can help by supporting individuals who are in denial while refraining from countenancing their self-deceptive thinking.

Second, recognize that the individual is struggling to cope with reality. We all do this in different ways. How we react to the diagnosis of someone we love varies to the degree that individual personalities vary. You may be acutely aware of symptoms; another family member may not be in the same psychological place. Ask yourself how important is it that the family member who is denying a problem exists acknowledges the problem right now. If you have shared your concerns about the situation, give other family members time to digest your concerns.

Third, denial is frequently not eliminated by simply confronting the individual who denies there is a problem. You know your family members. Take into consideration individual and family history of addressing problems. How can you best address the issue without inflaming new or reactivating old quarrels? Would bringing in a professional, clergy member, support group, or a family friend who has experience with Alzheimer's in the family, or some other means help gently move the individual out of denial? It may not always be possible to avoid confronting the denial.

Think ahead of time what you can do to help move your family member along without pushing that person to become overly defensive and further entrenched in his or her position.

The Obstacles: Fear

So many of our conscious or unconscious fears and anxieties have to do with serious illness and death that it is very normal to have these emotions awakened when some we love is diagnosed with Alzheimer's disease. Concrete fears based on what is known about Alzheimer's and what one might expect during the course of the disease, as well as how the family will handle the various difficulties when there is someone with Alzheimer's in the family, are coupled with fears that sometimes arise about mortality—our own and that of the people we love.

David Kessler in his book, *Life Lessons*, speaks of anger. He says,

> Untreated fear turns into anger. When we're not in touch with our fears—or when we don't even know we're afraid—that fear grows into anger. If we don't deal with the anger, it will turn into rage.
>
> We're more accustomed to dealing with our anger than with our fear. It's easier for us to say to a spouse "I'm angry at you" than it is to say "I'm afraid you'll leave." It's easier to get angry about what's going wrong than to admit "I am afraid I'm not good enough." (pp. 150-151)

Fear can manifest in many ways. When the individual with Alzheimer's disease does something potentially dangerous, you may react quickly with something resembling anger, and you may feel angry. Underlying the anger, though, is fear. If you have interacted with children, think of the times that you reacted with a quick flash of what looked like anger but which, in reality, was an alarm response when a child was about to do something dangerous. Your alarm response likely upset and frightened the child—it will do the same to a person with Alzheimer's.

Fear: Some Solutions and Coping

Most of us can understand and relate to the feeling of being afraid. It touches us and we respond. If, however, we are met with anger or even rage, we do not respond with outreached arms. For this reason it is so important to address what you are feeling. We've talked often about anger because it so easily erupts during the stressful times in our lives. Look deeper, and if it is fear that is manifesting itself in an angry response, try to understand and address the fear directly rather than letting it manifest in other ways.

Try to address your fears so that they are not given free reign to magnify or creep into your behavior disguised as other emotions. It may help you to start small—face your smaller, more concrete fears before tackling the big ones. You will feel more confident about your ability to succeed when you have successfully conquered some of your smaller fears.

Some degree of fear lingers for most of us. The unknown is frightening, and Alzheimer's certainly presents us with uncertainties. Fears of illness and death are daunting for many people and many theoreticians believe these are base fears that guide much of our behavior. Certainly, if you talk to people who have faced those fears head on by coming near to death, many have dispelled those fears and are able to live fuller, richer, and less self-limited lives as a result.

We cannot change the fact that we will die and the people we love will die. What we can change is how we live our lives while we are here, and how we love the people around us while they are here. Fearing our joint inevitable outcome will not change that outcome, but it will affect the quality of your life while you are living.

Deborah Recalls Experiences with Anxiety and Fear

I grouped these two psychological reactions because they feed on one another. Where there is anxiety there is fear. I tried my best to hide both fear and apprehension because I wanted to be the strong one. Finally, unable to hold it in any longer I would be purged through tears and long talks with my husband.

As a writer and an artist I tend to "see" things happening in my mind. My most persistent fear was my father wandering away and searching for his way back home. With such a mental picture in my head I found it difficult to get a good night's sleep. I would wake up and think about the worst case scenario of Dad hopelessly lost.

I had a lot of anxiety as each day was a trial to keep one step ahead of Dad. Somewhere along the way I developed the habit of carrying my portable telephone everywhere I went. Even though Dad has passed away I still find myself with the telephone in hand as I move through my day.

My anxiety was increased when Dad could no longer express himself and we were left to guess what he was thinking. Was he in pain or simply wanting to speak to us? I have a hard time accepting that I can't fix everything and as his illness took more and more of him I became more anxious. I wondered if I would be up to the ultimate task of letting him go. I think I feared being emotional in front of people. My pain was a private matter and I wasn't about to let anyone see my tears or know that I wasn't as strong as they thought I was.

A late night phone call, a call from the nursing home, a change in his condition, all of these situations would send my heart into a frenzy. You find yourself bracing for the worst and exhausted when you discover there is no emergency. Eventually there is an emergency and you are weak with fear. How do you prepare? I don't think you really can. You just do your best to let go of those reactions as quickly as you can and reserve your strength for the next time.

The Obstacles: Caregiver Stress

Stress is mentioned often through this book for a reason: few situations are more stressful than having serious chronic and terminal illnesses in the family. Alzheimer's is both chronic and terminal; an individual can live as long as twenty years with Alzheimer's, yet it is also progressive and eventually terminal.

Stress can show itself in a variety of ways, often disguising itself so that we do not recognize it for what it is. Often, it makes itself known physically through symptoms such as high blood pressure, headaches, other body aches, fatigue, stomach ailments, and other physical symptoms. Left unchecked, stress can lead to serious physical problems. It is therefore important to recognize stress and do something to alleviate its effects.

Everyone experiences stress, but Alzheimer's caregivers have more than their fair share. What differs about people who successfully find their way through the stresses of life versus those who are more easily overwhelmed by stress, is the way that stress is handled. Most people can learn to handle stress more effectively—it takes practice and a conscious decision to change the ways in which we perceive and respond to stressors.

Perception is a significant contributor to how we view the world and individual stressors. If the stressor, its import, and its ability to overwhelm us are perceived in an exaggerated light, it will seem more overwhelming and insurmountable. If, though, you try to put matters that are causing stress into perspective and prioritize, some of them will slip away into relative unimportance. This will leave you greater energy to focus on issues that are truly pressing. The degree of any given stressor can also be inflated beyond what is realistic—a temporary financial setback is viewed as financial ruin, a temporary change in your loved one's behavior is interpreted as a permanent downturn in her or his condition, and so on. Again, it is the interpretation of the stressor that causes most of the stress, not the actual stressor itself.

Caregiver Stress: Some Solutions and Coping

There are certainly a multitude of variables that can cause stress for Alzheimer's caregivers. It is physically, financially, emotionally, socially, and cognitively demanding. To cope with all of these stressors, you must recognize and address them. Letting them accumulate and fester will be damaging to you and your caregiving abilities. Below are methods of stress relief. Adapt them for your particular style, use as many as necessary to achieve stress-relief, and find methods of your own that work for you to relieve stress.

Try to avoid negative responses to stress. Some of the negative responses that are common among Western societies include alcohol and other substance abuse, overeating and eating food that is comforting but not particularly nutritious, and shopping or impulse buying to the extent that it can affect your financial well-being. Most of these provide only temporary stress relief and, if overused, can add to your stress by adding unnecessary physical and financial stress.

You have likely learned during the course of your lifetime what stress relievers work best for you. To be effective, individualize your stress relief to meet your needs and personality. Some effective stress-relieving techniques include:

1   Knowing your limitations. This has been discussed in some detail previously. Know when you have reached your limits regarding stress—failure to do so will hurt you and could lead to abusive behaviors when you are dealing with your affected loved one.

2   Plan ahead. You know that stressors will arise and often can anticipate what the stress will be. When it comes to caregiving, this means planning ahead for how to deal with financial issues, the physical demands of caregiving, for the cognitive challenges you may face, and for the emotional strain. As in all of life, some things can't be predicted. You can, however, plan how you will deal with stress as it arises by learning and using stress relief techniques and making them a part of your life to the degree that it will be almost second nature to rely on them when you most need them.

3   Uncertainty about the future can cause significant anxiety and stress. There will always be uncertainty about the future, whether there is a person in the family who has Alzheimer's

disease or not. To cope with uncertainty, continue to do what you are currently doing: educate yourself about Alzheimer's disease and, to the extent possible, prepare yourself for what is to come. It is always different when it is *your* loved one involved and there will likely be events for which you haven't prepared yourself, but the more you can prepare yourself for the future the better. Note that preparing yourself is vastly different from worrying about the future and stewing about it. The latter is stress inducing and counter-productive. There is a great deal of power in the thoughts contained in the Serenity prayer used by Alcoholic Anonymous and other groups—paraphrased, it advises us to do our best to control the things that we can control, let go of the things that we cannot control, and the wisdom to know the difference between the two.

4   Maintain a healthy diet. Eating "comfort food" now and then is fine, but the more that you can eat a healthy, balanced diet the better it is for your overall health and ability to cope with stress. Foods and substances high in the following substances tend to compound the effects of stress by stimulating the same chemical substances and bodily functions as stress itself: caffeine, sugar, nicotine, alcohol, and sodium (salt).

5   Exercise. For many people exercise is one of the most effective means of relieving stress and maintaining good emotional health. Research has shown that brain chemistry changes in ways that improve your sense of well-being and overall mental health. It is one of the few things that we do in life that is good for almost every aspect of your health, both mental and physical. Care giving also tends to lead to a tendency to isolate oneself, and finding ways to exercise outside of the house, even by taking walks with a friend, is an excellent way to avoid isolation that can lead to and intensify depression and other effects of stress. Yoga is an excellent formalized exercise routine when it comes to maintaining health and reliving stress.

6   Work on your attitude. Negative thinking is destructive and
serves no purpose other than to make you feel worse about
your situation and the world around you. As discussed before,
you must be realistic about your ability to undertake care
giving. If you think negatively about the situation you now
find yourself in without honest appraisal of the situation,
you're not being honest with yourself or realistic. If your
realistic appraisal tells you that some or all of the tasks of
care giving are beyond your capabilities, then give yourself
credit for being honest with yourself and work from that
premise. If you simply tend to work from an "I can't"
perspective, learn to challenge your negative thought
patterns. Catch your pattern at its beginning and counteract
you negative thoughts with more positive ones. If it helps,
write both down. If you tend toward the negative, you may
have to work to find more positive thoughts to
counterbalance the negative ones. The positives are there
but some people have to work harder to find them. Use
positive self-talk if it helps: tell yourself that you *can* do
things rather than you can't, that you are capable, and so
on. And do not dwell on your failures. You will have them—
everyone does. If you dwell on them they will magnify,
overshadow your successes, and lead to negative thinking
patterns.

7   Do not avoid your emotions. You are in a situation in which
strong emotions will sometimes arise and you must
acknowledge and deal with them. Denying their existence
will lead to those emotions coming out in other ways and a
tendency to feel more easily overwhelmed. The emotions
that you have denied and suppressed are underlying the
stress that piles on top of them, leading to an additive effect
that can feel suffocating after a while.

8   Engage in leisure and recreational activities. You need to
find a balance in your life and leisure/recreation should be a
part of that balance. If you allow your entire life to be
consumed by care giving, it will show in your stress level
and your care giving abilities.

9 Avail yourself of respite care, adult dare care services, and other services that are available in your community. More is covered on this topic in a separate section detailing care options. Take the breaks offered by these services and find ways to do things that bring you pleasure and some stress relief during these breaks.

10 Don't forget to laugh. Despite all of the stressors in the life of a caregiver, humor and laughter must remain a part of your life and part of the life of the person with Alzheimer's disease.

11 Use established stress management techniques and/or healthy ones that have a history of being an effective means of stress relief for you. Techniques including deep breathing and breathing control, progressive muscle relaxation, guided imagery, and stress inoculation are just some of the methods currently in use. You can learn these techniques in one or two sessions with a professional, videotapes are available to teach the techniques, and there are books on the market that also teach the techniques. Although it may be harder to learn any of these techniques properly through books, if that is your only alternative it is better than not using any method at all to relieve stress.

We have alluded occasionally to your care giving abilities deteriorating if you do not deal with your stress level, as well as to learning what your warning signs are for all sorts of situations, including stress overload. If you find that you are showing a number of these signs, it is time to reevaluate your situation, get assistance for yourself, get assistance with care giving, and actively address your stress level. If you are showing signs of burnout, which may include acting in abusive ways toward the individual with Alzheimer's disease, it is time to consider alternatives to you being the primary caregiver. Here are some of the signs of stress overload and burnout:

1 New physical problems or exacerbations of old ones such as high blood pressure, digestive problems, sleep difficulties, headaches, muscle tension leading to discomfort and other

problems, and so on. Any of these are signs that you need to find ways to decrease the ways in which stress is affecting you.

2   Feeling chronically mentally and physically exhausted.

3   Chronic anger, depression, worry, anxiety, or irritability. Become easily angered with the individual who has Alzheimer's is a sure sign that you are approaching burnout and need assistance or a complete break from caregiving.

4   Significant and chronic changes in your sleep patterns.

5   Increasingly isolating yourself and your loved one.

6   Acting out toward the person with Alzheimer's disease. This may include withholding care, intense anger at the individual who has put you in your current position, actively or passively withholding seeking medical attention when it is needed, and physically striking the person. If you have experienced this degree of stress, you have reached burnout and it is time to take a break from caregiving and consider alternate arrangements for your loved one.

If you have reached your limit and have to consider alternate caregiving arrangements for your loved one, do *not* consider it a failure. To the contrary, you should congratulate yourself for your honest appraisal of the situation and your ability to do what you need to in order to obtain the best care for the person you love.

The Obstacles: Depression, Anxiety, and Other Psychological Conditions

Rates of depression and anxiety are significantly higher among caregivers than among the general population. While depression and anxiety may be present in approximately two to nine percent of the general population at any given time (DSM-IV), rates have been estimated at between forty-six to fifty-nine percent of caregivers experience a clinical depression (references). People who have a history of past psychological conditions are more likely to experience a clinically significant psychological condition than people who have with no past history of psychological problems. Some conditions, such as depression, can occur for the first time at any age. Some can be precipitated by stress and distress, with depression again a prime example.

Everyone experiences difficult days and will feel "depressed" at times. Recognizing the difference between having the occasional "down" day or feeling normal levels of anxiety when faced with situations most people would find anxiety provoking. Clinically significant conditions such as depression and anxiety are different by virtue of the degree, clustering of symptoms and the perception of those symptoms, and longevity of symptoms. Whereas a "down" day may be followed by better days, for someone who is depressed any respite from symptoms tends to be brief if it occurs at all.

Depression may express itself differently among different people, including often differently between males and females. Where females may show symptoms more consistent with withdrawal, males may be more likely to act out, abuse substances such as alcohol, and exhibit anger. These are not hard and fast rules, though, and depression may be expressed a number of different ways by different people. The symptoms of depression for most people are as follows; to be diagnosed with depression an individual must experience at least five of the symptoms for at least a two week period and one or both of the first two symptoms listed here must be present.

1   Depressed mood. In children, adolescents, and some adults the mood may be irritable rather than depressed.
2   Significant loss of interest in most activities, even those one normally finds pleasurable.
3   Frequent crying. Often people find that they cry for what they report is "no reason." When more carefully analyzed, precipitants for the upset can often be identified.
4   Sleep disturbances. Changes in sleep can include waking frequently during the night, often with worrying or ruminating about problems accompanying awake periods;

early morning waking (at least two hours before your norm); hypersomnia (sleeping or wanting to sleep most of the time); changes in sleep habits so that an individual is, for example, awake most of the night and sleeping most of the day; overall insomnia.

5   Weight changes. Significant (5% of body weight) changes in weight and appetite. This can be either weight loss or weigh gain.

6   Changes in motoric behavior. You or others may notice that you appear lethargic, slowed in your actions, even your speech may be slowed ore become more halting; alternatively, your actions are more agitated—you pace, can't sit still for more than a few minutes, and so on.

7   Difficulty concentrating and making decisions. You may find yourself experiencing memory problems and may be distractible.

8   Thoughts about your own death. When someone in the family has a terminal illness, it is normal for thoughts about one's own mortality to surface. With depression, though, the thoughts are more centered around guilt and depressive themes, such as the family being better off without you and wishes for your own death. Thoughts about suicide are serious and indicate a need for professional attention.

9   Fatigue and loss of energy. This is a difficult issue for caregivers, whose time tends to be filled with work, family demands, the usual daily chores that take time and energy, and caregiving on top of common demands on time. You must, though, pay attention to what is normal for you and honestly assess if changes in your energy level are due to your stamina being overtaxed by the myriads of tasks you undertake daily or is due to a more intrinsic cause.

10 Some people may experience symptoms more strongly in the morning than at other times of day.

Depression can differ in degrees ranging from mild to severe. Sometimes, although rarely, depression can even be accompanied by psychotic symptoms such as delusions and hallucinations. Whether your depression is mild or severe, recognizing depression is an important first step to getting help. Research consistently supports the efficacy of therapy, medication, and particularly the combination of the two as treatments for depression.

Different cultures view therapy and the use of medications to treat psychological syndromes very differently. Although it has become more accepted in the United States, there are still many misconceptions about therapy and medications used for depression and other psychological conditions. In Western cultures, people often view conditions such as depression as simple weakness, a failure to "get it together" or "pull oneself up by one's bootstraps." This couldn't be more inaccurate. Psychological conditions are no different in many ways from medical illnesses that are more socially acceptable. When one has a medical condition, no one tells that person to "snap out of it." Yet this reaction is often faced by many people with depression and other conditions and, in fact, many think it themselves and thus contribute to their poor sense of self. Many psychological conditions are associated with changes in biochemistry and medication is designed to correct biochemical imbalances that may be associated with depression, anxiety, and other conditions. Antidepressants are not habit-forming or addictive; some anxiolytics (anti-anxiety medications) can be both habit-forming and addictive but if properly prescribed and monitored, are safe taken over short periods of time.

Most current therapy is brief and problem-focused for circumscribed problems such as a one-time depression and/or uncomplicated anxiety. We say "and/or" because depression and anxiety often coexist and you may be treated for symptoms of both if both are present. Longer therapy is generally reserved for more serious, chronic mental illnesses such as schizophrenia, bipolar disorder, and some personality disorders.

If you feel that you need professional assistance, ask your physician for a referral to a psychologist or clinical social worker. Friends and family members may also be a good resource. Although many clinicians will not treat individual members of the same family, a respected and trusted clinician may be able to make a referral to a colleague. Psychologists and clinical social workers will often work with your family physician if you have decided together that medication would help alleviate the symptoms of your condition or your physician may be more comfortable referring you to a psychiatrist for medication.

The symptoms of anxiety are more complex simply because "anxiety" as it is generally used actually encompasses a variety of different conditions, including but not limited to Generalized Anxiety Disorder, Panic Disorder, Posttraumatic Stress Disorder, Obsessive-Compulsive Disorder, Agoraphobia, and Specific Phobias. Generally, though, symptoms of anxiety are often physical in nature and may include the following (in general, at least four to six symptoms must be present for a diagnosis to be made):

1 For Generalized Anxiety Disorder, anxieties or worries that are unrealistic concerning at least two life circumstances for at least six months (e.g., worries about losing the family car without reason for those worries). Among family members of an individual with Alzheimer's disease, there are natural concerns—care issues, financial concerns, the health and well-being of your loved one, medical issues, and so on—all of these are normal concerns. How they are expressed and whether they are expressed as an actual anxiety disorder differentiates normal concerns from a clinical anxiety disorder.

2 Symptoms that indicate muscular tension. These may include tremulousness or feeling shaky. You may feel restless or jumpy.

3 Dizziness or feeling lightheaded.

4 Sweating without cause such as hot weather. You may also feel clammy or experience hot flashes or chills.

5 Shortness of breath and/or a feeling of tightness or discomfort in the chest. Heart rate often increases and palpitations may be experienced.

6   Some people experience gastrointestinal symptoms such as nausea, diarrhea, or vomiting. Frequent urination may also be a problem for some people.

7   Startling easily.

8   Irritability.

9   Difficulty concentrating when anxiety is present or elevated.

10 Feeling that you are choking or difficulty swallowing.

11 Fears including fear that you are going crazy, fears of dying, and so on.

12 Tingling or numbness in extremities.

13 If you are experiencing panic attacks, they typically have a sudden onset and are accompanied by feelings of terror or fear of an impending horrific event. Many people become more anxious and the panic elevates due to the physical symptoms of the attack, which many people interpret as having a heart attack or other similar acute medical problem.

14 Panic and anxiety often lead people to begin avoiding situations that cause anxiety or panic, sometimes leading people to avoid all public situations and becoming virtual shut-ins.

Clearly the symptoms of panic and anxiety warrant a physical exam to rule out any physical cause for such problems as chest discomfort and palpitations. Once a physical cause has been ruled out, your physician can make a referral to a mental health professional. Most anxiety can be very successfully treated with brief, problem-focused therapy.

Family in Crisis Mode

In some families, problematic family dynamics will come into play very early on. In other families the affected person may be well into the disease before such problems begin to be seen. In the very functional family, problems may not be an issue.

Ideally we would all come from a well-adjusted family of origin. We would all have loving parents and siblings who are able to care for one another and relate well to one another. The ideal is not everyone's reality. "Dysfunctional" is the term we hear all too often to describe families. The term is useful, in that it indicates a family with problems, but it encompasses a wide variety of different families and different problems. There is no such thing as a "normal" family, but there are families that function better than others. When serious pressures such as an illness in the family are introduced into family dynamics, these families tend to continue to function fairly well. If your family has a history problems functioning as a unitary system, be the problems tacit or glaring, those problems may surface again and intensify.

We frequently hear, "This is the time when we should all be pulling together," when a dementing or other illness is diagnosed. In the real world, families who have not been able to do so in the past are not likely to do so when a crisis arises, at least not for long periods of time. Many pull together and function well for a time, only to have long-standing family problems resurface and, as time goes on, escalate as resentments and anger build. Those families that do pull together and continue to function fairly well as a unit have probably, previously done so.

Now that your family is facing unusual pressure you may find that unresolved issues are bubbling to the surface. Feelings that you had as a child may inexplicably take on a new life and intermingle with your adult reactions. These emotions are important signals. They may, among other things, represent the unfinished business of childhood, the desire for some to return to the relative safety of childhood, may dredge up difficult feelings familiar during your childhood, or may bring back a visceral reminder of the sense of powerlessness you felt as a child.

Few events in life leave us feeling as powerless as a serious illness invading the body of someone we love. We want to "fix it," do something to make it "better," make it go away. And we cannot. Feeling powerless will likely be a recurring theme throughout the duration of your loved one's illness. You are powerless to affect a cure, to permanently alter the course of the disease, and thus to permanently change your loved one's future.

Similarly, many times as children we are powerless to change a situation or even express your attitude toward it. Since you are no longer a child. As an adult you have the power to make choices, and these choices are what separate you from the child you once were. You can choose to let yourself and your relationships continue to be dominated by the emotional baggage of this unfinished business or you can choose to break the dysfunctional cycle.

If you are the spouse of an Alzheimer's patient and you have believed all of your life that you are dependent on someone else for your survival now, is a crucial time. You must do an internal inventory and realize that you do have strengths. Build on those strengths and work on your weaknesses. The first step is opening up your inner shelves and looking to see what is inside. Your shelves are not bare no matter how empty you feel. Look inside with the brightness of reality, not the dim glimpse of fear. There is strength there, that will be the foundation upon which you build the rest of your life. You are not a victim, you are a survivor.

GRIEF

Grieving the Loss of the Living

Perhaps the hardest thing to accept about Alzheimer's disease is that people with it are leaving us a little more everyday. It is a slow motion death and slow motion grief. The spouse of an Alzheimer's patient losses the companionship, intimacy, protection, and shared memories of their marriage. Adult children find their parent shifting roles, slowly becoming effectively the child in the relationship. Memories of all of those relationships are slowly diminishing and, eventually, disappearing. Sometimes in the middle stages you may even want to take the person with Alzheimer's by the shoulders and shake him and insist that he snap out of it. He looks fine! Why can't he remember?

In the later stages it is like going to their wake with every visit. They lie there unable to communicate. They stare with eyes that

have lost all their sparkle. They are disconnected from the world
and yet, they live.

When someone dies there is finality. There is a ceremony and
a tribute to that individual's life. The world seems to pause and let
you put the period at the end of the sentence. You look back over
the life the person led and you say goodbye. There is sorrow and
the grieving process continues. You miss having her in your life.
You miss the sound of that person's voice and the way you felt
when you were reflected back in her eyes.

With Alzheimer's disease you miss the communication. You
want to ask them "what are you thinking about," but their answer
doesn't make sense if there is an answer at all. You don't see yourself
reflected in their eyes because they have forgotten you and your
relationship to them. The world doesn't pause and give you closure.
You go on each day missing them, grieving the loss of them and
visiting them.

In *Life* Lessons, Elisabeth Kubler-Ross notes the following:

> Losing those we love to death is certainly one of the
> most heartbreaking experiences. An interesting comment,
> made with no disrespect to anyone, is that people who lose
> someone through divorce or separation will often say that
> they realize death is not the ultimate loss. Rather, it's the
> separation from the loved ones that is so difficult. Knowing
> about someone's continued existence but being unable to
> share it with them may cause far more pain and make
> resolution far more difficult than permanent separation
> through death. With those who have died, however, we
> find new ways to share their existence as they live on in our
> hearts and memories.

The fact that Alzheimer's disease, by its very nature separates
affected people from the realities of their world it is extremely hard
to accept. We can see them, touch them, hold them but not *have*
them. They are separated from us by the unseen damage of
dementia.

Among families of people with Alzheimer's disease, there are commonalities enough to make bonds where none previously existed and create a shorthand language built of knowing that which is shared among the families of Alzheimer's sufferers. The individual differences, though, remain and make each family unique just as they do each family member. Some have been letting go for a while, knowing that their loved one is nearing the end of his life. Others are not ready to let go until their loved one dies. The road to the end stages of Alzheimer's may have been long or relatively brief, although nothing about Alzheimer's disease ever seems brief.

Families who have talked openly about life and death will fare better during the later stages of Alzheimer's disease. Knowing what your affected loved one wants, what she values as quality of life, how she wants to live and die will make this painful process far more peaceful and loving than will lack of preparation. As suggested elsewhere in the book, it is essential to have prepared for the time when your loved one can no longer voice her wishes. A clear and precise living will gives family members enormous peace of mind. As in other decisions you make, there may be those who second guess decisions you make about care in these later stages, including such practical issues as feeding tubes and respirators. A clear living will prevents, or at least minimizes the power, of detractors at this stage. And you will be able to make difficult decisions with the peace of knowing that you are fulfilling your loved one's wishes.

The question of protecting children often arises again during the later stages of Alzheimer's disease. As was true in earlier stages, it is generally a mistake to shelter children from the truth. Remember, children's imaginations can sometimes be far more powerful and frightening than reality. Children who are cognitively able should be allowed to make these decisions with you and should be allowed to spend time with a dying grandparent if the child wants to do so. Children will let you know, verbally or nonverbally, when they are uncomfortable and do not wish to be near the person with Alzheimer's. Be sensitive to their desires and their signals. Adapt communications to their developmental levels. Answer questions honestly, answering only the question that has been asked and no more—do not overload or embellish with information the child has not sought.

When someone we love is consumed by a lengthy illness, part of us wishes our loved one would live on and part hopes for death and release from, what many see as a prison for those we love. Too often we have heard people say, "It's a terrible thing to say, but I wish he would die." It is not a terrible thing to say or to think. Not only is it normal, it is a loving thing to say. Who of us wants to see someone we love suffer and live in a way that we know he or she would loathe? Part of loving is being willing to let go when the time is right, whether it is of a young adult who is ready to leave home or a parent who has reached the natural end of his life.

Death and the Grief That Follows

Grief may start at any time during these later stages as your loved one loses the ability to maintain basic life-sustaining functions. You may grieve the person who has been lost to Alzheimer's disease long before there is a physical death. And then there is grief after that person has died. Although there are some differences, the processes are essentially the same.

One of the foremost experts in the field of bereavement or grief is Elisabeth Kubler-Ross. In her many books, she speaks about the stages of grief, which she maintains progress in order: denial, anger, bargaining, depression, and acceptance (e.g., 1969). Others have suggested different stages and progressions. While many people may experience grief in this orderly fashion, more recent research (e.g., Wortman & Silver, 1989) suggests that grief is not quite so orderly and that emotions ebb and flow over time—old emotions may have brief resurgences, particularly during days with special meaning for the deceased and his family, and early in the course of grief one may find respite from its pain without going through all of the "stages." Research by Wortman and Silver (1989) and others suggests that some people experience few, and occasionally no emotional disruptions at all, following the death of a family member.

Their research also shows that, contrary to popular belief, that these people often fare well in the psychological aftermath. It was previously believed that such reactions would herald a delayed and complicated grief process. While this may be true for some individuals, it clearly it is not an inevitable certainty.

Some specialists in the field have also contended that grief that is not fully worked through and experienced according to a set progression of stages, with each relatively completed before beginning the next, will become a pathological grief process that may be prolonged and may involve pathological psychological processes, such as a clinical depression.

Current research supports a process that is more individualized and may not look at all like the stage models with which people may be more familiar. There often are significant individual differences in the grief process. Some may experience grief in stages, others may find themselves experiencing the different grief responses on and off during the process.

Anger, sadness, guilt, loneliness, transient depressed feelings, searching, expecting to hear or see your loved one, bargaining, acceptance, and so many other reactions are all within the norm, and these may wax and wane for a period of time. There is some agreement in the literature that, in general, grief should resolve within about a year. Note, though, that this standard refers to the active grieving process and to the loss of an older person after an extended illness. Other types of losses are associated with other kinds of grieving experiences. Putting a time limit on grieving is meant to provide a guideline, not an absolute end to grief. Birthdays, anniversaries, holidays, and the anniversary of your loved one's death may awaken fresh but very brief bouts of grief.

Active grieving that continues to interfere with one's ability to function after a year is an indication that the grief process is no longer a normal one and that professional psychological assistance may be warranted. There can be many reasons for unresolved grief or grief that evolves into a clinically significant psychologically process: a highly ambivalent relationship with the deceased, previous psychological difficulties, and previously unresolved grief, are just some of the factors that have been associated with abnormal grief processes.

People often report feeling relieved when they learn how normal it is to have different experiences during the grieving process. Many have stated that they thought they "were going crazy." Until they understand that their grief may be associated with psychological phenomena that are new to the individual or which do not follow what they have been told is the "normal" path. Occasionally people even relate experiences of seeing or hearing the person who has died. Although generally a vague impression, it can be a quite vivid experience for some people. How one interprets these events depends on the individual and, often, his spiritual beliefs. What is important to know, though, is that this is not an indication that one is "going crazy." One interpretation that may be offered is that this often occurs during times when one expects to see his loved one (e.g., during the time she returned home after work each day) and the mind almost literally anticipates the vision or sound of that person. However one makes sense of these incidents, unless there are other indications of psychological disturbance of a clinically significant degree, this is a part of the grieving process that may be considered within the normal range.

When considering the ability to weather the grieving process, different factors may come into play for different people. These become relevant to families when considering how a loved one may need support following the death of a spouse. For example, men may need more support with household management and women with financial management. Research show these to be different stressors and are sometimes associated with the development of depression after being widowed (e.g., Umberson, Wortman, & Kessler, 1992). The specific stressors may be different for your family members. It is important to take into consideration the practical issues that may be problematic for the affected family members and to provide assistance in whatever way possible. Doing so may prevent future practical and emotional problems.

We often gather before and immediately after the death of a friend and family member and then gravitate back to our busy lives. This is normal and healthy. However, this often leaves family members of the person who has died, particularly the spouse, alone and adrift. Family members and friends can help by being aware of this common occurrence and continuing to provide social and emotional support through this period of adjustment. How much support will be needed, as well as the nature of the support, will depend on your family and the individuals who are impacted.

Personal Experience with Grief

Grief is defined as sorrow, heartache and despair. When I think of the grief I have for my father I know that I have grieved throughout his illness. I grieved each time he lost the ability to do something that we all take for granted. I grieved when I saw him use the wrong end of a screwdriver to loosen a screw. Each time he looked at me with puzzlement as if to ask "what is happening to me?" I grieved. I longed for a way to rescue him.

The beginning was like the end. I wanted to fix it when he was diagnosed, I wanted to fix it when I saw him lying there so helpless and hear him struggling to breathe through the rattle in his lungs, and I wanted to fix it when he died. But, most of all, I wanted it to be over for him.

Now that Dad has died I try to remember him as he was before the disease stole parts of his brain. I try but it is so hard to do. I try to remember his bright blue eyes and his wonderful sense of humor but instead visions of him bumping into walls in that damned baby walker creep back into my head.

It wasn't until he reached the very end that I understood Rose's letter to her father. She wrote "I'm glad you are dead because you are not the man I know you to be." Dad was no longer the man he wanted to be. He wasn't free. He was a prisoner in a body that had betrayed him.

I have not been back to the nursing home where Dad died. I truly believe that part of me would expect to see him in his room waiting for a kiss and hug. I guess that is my silly way of coping with his death. I believe he is in Heaven but I also keep a little niche of my brain convinced that he is in room 6 on the left side of the hall.

I have days when I smile remembering him and days when I can barely stand to think about him. When I was grieving for him as he was in the last stage I learned that the best place to sob is in the shower. I learned the best place to scream when a scream is all that will do is inside a moving car. You will find your own means of releasing your sorrow.

I wrote a letter to My Dad and placed it inside his casket. It simply said "You were a Good Dad and I love you so much." That is about all there is to say I suppose. My husband's parents have passed away and even after years he says there are times when he expects them to call or stop by. Maybe that is a gift, a way of keeping them alive in our hearts.

References

Kubler-Ross, E. (1969). *On death and dying.* New York: Macmillan.

Kubler-Ross, E. & Kessler, D. (2000). *Life Lessons.* New York: Scribner.

Wortman, C.B. & Silver, R.C. (1989). The myths of coping with loss. *Journal of Consulting and Clinical Psychology, 57(3),* 349-357.

Umberson, D., Wortman, C.B., & Kessler, R.C. (1992). Widowhood and depression: explaining long-term gender differences in vulnerability. *Journal of Health and Social Behavior, 33(1),* 10-24.

Psychological Aspects of Alzheimer's Disease

We cannot fully know what it is like to have Alzheimer's disease unless we have walked in those footsteps. But we can imagine and, more importantly, we can listen and learn from people who do have the disease.

One of the greatest fears for many people is fear of losing oneself, one's identity. Much depends on how much the person who has been diagnosed knows about the disease—there is fear of the known and fear of the unknown. The potential of losing touch with the connections to the people we love in the world is as resounding a fear as the changes that will occur internally. We all must remember that while fear of the future is present, not allowing that daunting future overcome all quality of present life is a key to well being—being able to live today is critical.

People with Alzheimer's want the same basic qualities in life that they always did, the same ones most of us strive for—feeling that we are worthwhile and valued, feeling that we love and are loved in return, feeling safe, feeling competent and capable, being treated with respect and dignity, and so on. They want to lead meaningful lives and many who are early in the course of the disease when they are diagnosed are able to readjust their priorities and interpretation of what it means to be a worthwhile person in a way that is more congruent with their new reality, and in a way that others can learn from. One of the things we have found is that slowing to the pace of people who have cognitive challenges can bring a sense of peace and liveliness to the things around us that we had previously ignored. In a marvelous example of reframing the way she was now seeing the world, Lorrain Smith who is diagnosed with early onset Alzheimer's wrote:

> I've noticed that I have a large amount of appreciation
> for whatever I'm focused on, it is very clear and very real.
> Look away and it is gone. Look back and it is fresh and new.
> I am checking this out with a red geranium blossom right
> now. When I look away 'red' no longer exists except as an
> abstract term. No blossom image remains. But I can look
> again . . .

People with Alzheimer's feel a full range of emotions and a majority of people with early to moderate Alzheimer's attach meaning and reason to the emotions. Some people with even moderate levels of Alzheimer's say that they come to realize that, while losses may be significant by that point, they realize that they can still feel the joy of playing with a grandchild, the warmth of an embrace that conveys love, and the passion of holding the hand of a spouse. We want to be careful here not to impose unrealistic expectations on any individual, but at the same time remind all of those who care for people with Alzheimer's not to discount their full range of human emotions and possibilities.

The diagnosis of Alzheimer's disease is devastating. Yet, to a significant proportion of people, it is also ironically a little comforting, if only temporarily. Most have been experiencing the symptoms of Alzheimer's for a while before diagnosis, and may have been going through various kinds of medical and neuropsychological testing. Through all of this, many people with Alzheimer's voice that they have felt they were going "crazy" and there was no other reason for the symptoms they have been experiencing. And because of issues such as misconceptions about aging and denial, the problems being experienced by the individual with Alzheimer's may have been minimized or dismissed by others. When the individual has been aware of the difficulties she has been experiencing, having her concerns dismissed or minimized is demoralizing and confusing, and it contributes to the perception that she is just "going crazy" when others do not take that person seriously. Conversely, people who are aware that they are having problems and fear the worst may avoid seeing a doctor and may be overwhelmed by the diagnosis.

Reaction to the diagnosis varies—disbelief, a sense of numbness, and denial are common, as are anger and distress. It is a dynamic process, one that requires adaptation to a new reality. Depression is very common among people with Alzheimer's disease and it may require treatment with antidepressant medications and, optimally, counseling as well. The apathy and lack of initiation seen in many people with Alzheimer's can be caused by the disease, but it can also be caused by depression. An evaluation by a neurologist, neuropsychologist, or a neuropsychiatrist (a psychiatrist who specializes in treating people with underlying neurological conditions) can help to detect depression when it is present. If left untreated, depression can cause impairments not caused by the Alzheimer's itself but exaggerating Alzheimer's symptoms. The majority of people who have Alzheimer's without clinically significant depression and/or anxiety added into the mix tend to lead fulfilling lives in the early stages of the disease; many people report that they are determined to live the best lives they can while they are able to and will not let a daunting future destroy the present.

Other events can be as devastating as the diagnosis. Many people, particularly those who have been gainfully employed most of their adult lives, report that the day that they have to stop working and the day that they are approved for disability were as horrendous for them as the day they were diagnosed. It is a cementing of the diagnosis, an official acknowledgment of one's impairments and new status as someone who warrants disability support.

Despite the diagnosis being a terrible one to hear and to live with, like so many people with serious illnesses, people diagnosed with Alzheimer's can be remarkably resilient. Previous ability to cope with adversities in life, as well as coping style, will help to determine individual responses. Even people who were not particularly spiritual may turn to spiritual explorations to help understand and cope with the disease and find solace in the exploration if not the answers to their existential kinds of questions. Family and friends often provide invaluable emotional support and people with Alzheimer's report that this kind of emotional support helps immeasurably when it comes to coping and adjusting to the disease. Among people who cope well, many voice the simple truism that they must find ways to cope—they do not have a choice about having the disease and so must make the best of the time that they have and do the best that they can within the confines of their disease characteristics. These people certainly have some days that are harder than others, become frustrated and angry, and the like. One difference between these individuals and people who are more overwhelmed is that people who fare better find ways to make good days and find proactive ways to cope. Some of the proactive measures we have heard people use include keeping a journal, seeking individual or family therapy, finding ways to compensate for deficits, attending support groups, becoming active in Alzheimer's advocacy groups, information seeking, and so on.

Even the most resilient person struggles at times as exemplified by the following written by Morris Friedell:

> However, taking a hard look, I see that I nevertheless have been declining. Visual processing, conversation, or taking initiative is more fatiguing. I feel yet more deeply like an interstellar voyager, or like on of the dead in Our Town.
>
> I probably won't be dying soon, but I'm not 'living' either. Hardly anything ever happens in my life anymore, and that's not likely to change. I can perhaps further patch myself up with rehab—but how long will I be able to hold out with any quality of life? The future is a dark cloud. (*http://members.aol.com/MorrisFF/*)

Dr. Friedell is a retired sociology professor diagnosed with early onset Alzheimer's disease over three years prior to writing the above passage. He continues to engage in constructing a well thought out rehabilitation paradigm for person with dementia and to write about his cognitive and emotional experiences as he lives with Alzheimer's. His resiliency and courage are remarkable, including his willingness to share his struggles as well as his triumphs.

Clearly as time progresses the ability to engage in these kinds of coping strategies dwindles and eventually disappears, although they can be kept up for a fair amount of time when there is family and community support. And this will vary—some people with Alzheimer's are higher functioning in the early to middle stages than others. It may well be that the majority of people who are higher functioning during these stages were very cognitively active during their adult lives and remain so in the early and even middle stages of the disease. Note that, as we have said repeatedly throughout this book, ability to control and understand emotions is increasingly out of the control of people with Alzheimer's disease and ability to use coping strategies will wane rapidly for some people, more slowly for others. We need to attend to individual characteristics unique to our loved ones and stay open to all possibilities.

Fear can take up residence in the person with Alzheimer's even before a diagnosis is made. When symptoms start to become apparent enough that one begins getting lost in familiar environments and other problems begin to assert themselves, fear that it might be Alzheimer's causing the problems if the individual is aware of Alzheimer's symptoms, fear that one is going crazy, fear of getting a diagnosis and fear of not learning what is causing the problems, and fear about the future are just some of the issues that arise. There are so many more—fear that one will be abandoned, fear of abuse or neglect in the hands of institutional caregivers (or, sometimes, family), fear that one will be diminished in the eyes of others, fear that one will embarrass oneself, fear of being a burden to loved ones, fear of losing oneself and connections to the world as Alzheimer's progresses, and ultimately fear of death.

Understanding that both immediate concrete issues are a source of fear and more existential fears (e.g., death) come into play can help caregivers communicate with people who have Alzheimer's.

Reassurance that the individual is and will continue to be safe, cared for, nurtured, and loved may have to be offered over and over as those reassurances are likely to be forgotten as time passes. As the disease progresses, fears that are expressed tend to be about immediate, concrete issues. Sometimes the concrete fears still express more global abstract fears, such as abandonment, but cannot be communicated in any but concrete, sometimes nonverbal ways. Imagine what it is like to be in a strange place surrounded by strangers, even when that place is home and the strangers are actually family members. And then to have those strangers try to undress and bathe you! It can be terrifying for Alzheimer's sufferers. We need to attend to both the concrete fears and the possibility that more abstract fears are being expressed.

Fears will be different at different stages of the disease, and even on different days and hours of the day as the symptoms fluctuate. Early in the disease, people are generally more able to reason through the fears, talk them through with family members and others, and think about the big picture. As the disease progresses, the fears that are communicated or displayed tend to be more concrete—fear that people are stealing from the individual, fear of specific events (e.g., bathing), and so on. The person's world is getting physically and emotionally smaller, and the fears that are displayed reflect that diminution.

It can be argued that those concrete fears that are seen later in the disease continue to reflect larger or more abstract fears. A repeated claim that a husband who visits daily has not been coming to visit his spouse in a nursing facility, for example, can be viewed as a specific claim about a specific issue that is forgotten due to poor memory or a larger fear and sense of abandonment. In this instance, arguing with the individual and trying to persuade her that the husband visits daily is likely futile and may cause more upset than it is worth. Reassurance that she is loved and will always be loved, and family will continue to visit her daily may be more effective—it addresses the concrete fear and a general fear of abandonment. In this instance, you may also try leaving a message for her on a board she can see (if she can still read) or other orienting message reminding her that the husband has been there and that he would return the next day may help, particularly if it is done routinely so that the individual with Alzheimer's gets used to looking for the message.

Loneliness can be overwhelming. People with Alzheimer's often isolate themselves and thus compound the sense of loneliness. Shame and embarrassment about deficits make it difficult for many people to be in public and interact with strangers, and sometimes friends and family. It is also an exhausting struggle to engage in the multiple cognitive tasks necessary when moving around in the environment. Insensitivities of people one encounters in public can make it feel even more daunting to venture out. Compound these with realistic concerns about getting lost when the individual with Alzheimer's is alone, the confusion that can occur when one does not recognize surroundings or is in busy surroundings, and for some a reluctance to ask friends and family for help, and it is easy to see why many people begin to increasingly isolate themselves. For others, increasing isolation may be more associated with depression, which by itself often leads people to isolate themselves. And finally, for some individuals lack of initiation and apathy, which may or may not be depression related, may be the cause of increased isolation.

Aside from a tendency to isolate, even when one is surrounded by others people with Alzheimer's can feel lonely just by virtue of having the disease. Support groups are often offered for caregivers— they are found far less frequently for people who actually have the disease. While it is true that later in the disease a support group would be futile, this is not the case earlier in the disease. It helps people with Alzheimer's and other diseases to talk to people who have walked similar paths, who understand their concerns, and who can speak a kind of shorthand because of shared experiences. Even Internet groups and message boards tend to be heavily dominated by caregivers despite many people with early stages of Alzheimer's using the Internet as a resource for support and information. The end result is that few people with Alzheimer's have the opportunity to talk to others in the same boat, which can feel lonely and isolating. It can feel lonely to simply have a serious illness—it separates people from those who do not have the illness, a sort of "us and them" feeling that can make people feel invisible and very alone.

Try to seek out online resources if you cannot find a support group near you, or if need be, try to start a group. Again, this is not a realistic goal later in the disease but for people with early to moderate Alzheimer's it can be a significant source of coping and connection.

A wonderful resource for people with Alzheimer's is a group started and run by persons with dementing conditions. The Dementia Advocacy and Support Network International (DANSI) is a terrific place to find individual and group support, including a chat room and links to eloquent and beautifully constructed personal pages, where many people have generously shared their journals. Most of the people who share their journals speak about the loneliness, depression, and anxiety they often feel and how these difficult emotions are often alleviated by keeping up with this marvelous group that offers mutual support. The group goes far beyond the website—they are active in dementia conferences, some members have testified before Congress, and some have published poetry, prose, scholarly works, and books about Alzheimer's.

To combat loneliness, friends and families can help by making sure that the individual knows he can talk about all issues, including his emotions, concerns, and fears. Knowing that family members and friends will listen without judging or demeaning feelings helps one to feel connected to those people and feel understood. This includes being open to all types of communications, including sometimes dark humor.

Humor can be used for a variety of reasons—it is a sophisticated defense mechanism, it may help to alleviate tension when people around the person with Alzheimer's are uneasy talking about it, it helps to alleviate tension in the individual using humor, and it is an effective means of opening communication. Caregivers need to make sure that humor does not make the person with Alzheimer's feel demeaned, but realize that humor may be used by the individual as a means of coping and communication, and will often be appreciated when it is used appropriately by family members and friends. A sense of humor is retained a long time among people with Alzheimer's—we all need to laugh and people with Alzheimer's and other diseases are no exception.

Frustration is a problem well into the course of the disease. Imagine forgetting how to tie your shoes or dress yourself and trying to complete those tasks. Imagine having to ask others to help you with the simplest of tasks, ones that the individual knows she could once accomplish easily. The potential for frustration is omnipresent as abilities wane.

Anger, too, may be one of the emotions your loved one experiences on and off during the course of the disease. When the individual is still able to process feelings linked with thoughts about having the disease, anger shares similar sources as that found in family members—anger at having the disease, anger at God for allowing it to happen, anger at people who are perceived to be demeaning or insensitive, and anger at others who do not suffer the same fate are just some sources that people with Alzheimer's express. Later in the disease, anger can flare easily—emotions are not under the same kind of control as they were when the individual was healthy. What may have been a minor irritation becomes a major flash point, a frustration may become a catastrophically angry reaction.

A great many things can cause sadness. As we age those of us fortunate enough to reach old age will lose many of our peers. Many people are left with few or no people with whom they share a history and a similar reference to the past. With Alzheimer's, people often have to give up their home and move in with relatives, into assisted living facilities, or to a nursing facility. Losing independence, including driving, is a source of sadness for many people. Surrendering so much of our lives and individuality may lead to many bouts of grief—giving up a loved pet, the independence of driving, moving away from a home one has lived in for many years . . . each loss, both big and what may seem small, can bring a fresh wave of grief.

There is a difference between empathizing with a person who has Alzheimer's or any other serious illness and thinking that you know what that individual goes through. The last thing most people with Alzheimer's wants to hear is "oh, I forget my (fill in the blank) all of the time. Don't think anything of it." It minimizes and dismisses the person, who then does not feel heard or understood. While it is usually an earnest attempt to communicate empathy or make the person feel better about mistakes, it is generally not heard that way.

Many people have a tendency to shun persons with Alzheimer's. It usually isn't intentional and it happens to people with serious illnesses all of the time. Particularly in the case of Alzheimer's disease, when others are aware of the nature of the disease they back away, emotionally if not physically. The individual and her attempts to connect too often are brushed aside, as if the disease is contagious or nothing that she has to contribute is worthwhile. People report they begin to feel invisible, insignificant, and diminished. Even when people with Alzheimer's have lost the memory of names and exact knowledge about the relationship they bear to the people around them, they never lose the need to connect to others.

Above all, leave the communication door open. Let your loved one know that you would like to talk about anything of concern to him and, more importantly, are there to listen. Not talking about the presence of a serious illness is like ignoring a huge elephant lying in the middle of your living room. Everyone sees it, trips over it, tiptoes around it, steps in its droppings and yet tries to pretend it is not there. It is there, and pretending it is not only makes its presence something dark and sinister.

We would like to end this section with words from Morris Friedell:

> Meanwhile, life goes on, albeit a diminished life. I believe in the Jewish ethic of kiddush hahayyim, the sanctification of life. Amidst the horrors of the ghettos and camps my people did not surrender easily but lived with hope and died with dignity, witnessing to our faith. I yet have life to

live, and word to do. I can apply more intensively my concepts of rehabilitation and psychotherapy, I can explore what Buddhist ideas about emptiness and impermanence have to offer. And I remain a participant in family, communities and the world. There are grandchildren to hug, there are others out there facing difficult situations I can yet say a word to.

Morris Friedell

Making Hard Choices

Throughout your loved one's illness you, the caregiver, will be faced with very hard choices. It will seem as though hardly a day passes that you aren't faced with a decision that may impact your future.

You may feel very isolated as you struggle with the options ahead of you. In the early stages you will be making decisions about when to contact a doctor, when to override your loved one's decision making, when to call on other family members for support. You may be leaning toward handling every decision on your own for as long as you can. Most people want to wait as long as possible before asking for help. A basic desire in many Western societies is to preserve our independence. At the same time, you are only one person and you will find yourself overwhelmed by the changes that lie ahead.

As soon as possible try to bring your family together and take a team approach. The more people you have who are working toward a common goal, the better chance you will have of proceeding without exhaustion.

At some point in your loved one's illness there will come a time when you will have to decide how his or her welfare will best be met. There are several options. When deciding which option to take remember that you can always change your mind. Learn as much as you can before making big decisions and think through the possible ramifications of your choices. Keep in mind that the fewer changes you have to make in the life of the person with Alzheimer's disease, the better. Change is upsetting for a person with Alzheimer's and can upset, behavioral disturbances, and downward spirals. Make changes very carefully. If you find that the changes you have made are a mistake, they can be corrected but, again, do so with forethought and carefully.

You may want to try, for instance, home health services. If this is affordable and works well for you, then it may be an option by which you are able to keep your loved one at home. If that does not meet your needs or you require more assistance, you might combine the use of home health aides during the evening or nighttime hours and adult daycare during the day. Cost will almost certainly enter into your decision making since most of the charges will be out of pocket.

As unlikely as it sounds you will find that the hardest decisions you make will be the subject of second-guessing. The second-guessing is heartbreaking and frustrating. If you have decided that the only option is admission to a nursing home, there will be people who will insist that your loved one could be living at home. Their words will cause you to wonder if you have made the wrong decision. At that point you will be glad that you have a support system whether it is a support group, family or trusted friends. Do not let the second-guessing undermine your self-confidence. No one can walk in your shoes during these difficult times, and you must make the best decisions you can based on your own circumstances.

Even at a point when Deborah's father required around the clock supervision, having to be physically lifted up from chairs, bed and bath, there were those who second-guessed her mother's decision to place him in a nursing home. They were not individuals who had been present during the family's struggle to keep him at home.

EXPLORING OPTIONS

There are a number of options to consider. Which you choose will likely be influenced by a combination of different factors: your loved one's care needs, ability of family and friends to provide care giving, availability of services in your community, and cost are some of the variables that will factor into your decision.

There are a number of different kinds of living and care options to consider as alternatives for people with Alzheimer's disease.

Alternate Living Arrangements:

1 Retirement communities generally require more independence. Those with anything other the earliest stages of Alzheimer's, should consider an alternative. Retirement communities usually consist of separate apartments and/or houses with a central area for community activities. Services are provided to make living independently easier (e.g., transportation) and the breadth of the services depends on the community. As the disease progresses, Retirement Communities are only realistic options if in-home, 24-hour care is arranged by family members.

2 Continuing Care Retirement Communities. These communities are designed to allow a range of care from completely independent living with a variety of services provided to fee-based assistance provided in the home to a nursing home affiliated with the facility. Like retirement communities, family participation is necessary to monitor the safety and well-being of the individual with Alzheimer's. Supervision and monitoring of care is up to families, even when paid caregivers are hired. In most retirement communities and senior facilities, there are limitations regarding who may live with the senior (e.g., no children under a certain age). These communities can be very expensive.

3 Senior housing facilities may offer separate apartments and community activities, but generally do not offer the kind of supervision a person with Alzheimer's needs as the disease progresses. Like retirement communities, Senior houseing facilities are appropriate in the later stages only if alternate care arrangements and 24-hour supervision are arranged by family members.

4   Assisted living facilities (ALFs). These may be an option for people with Alzheimer's disease as long as family members remain involved to assure quality of living and safety issues are addressed sufficiently. Types of ALFs range from single or shared bedrooms in a facility to independent apartments. Facilities typically have a dining room, space for arranged and informal social activities, and may have additional services available for a fee. ALFs do not require the same degree of independence as retirement communities and senior housing faculties. ALFs are licensed by state governments and, as part of the "assisted living," will monitor medications, provide routine medical assistance, and will assist with activities of daily living (ADLs, such as bathing and dressing). ALFs are not a substitute for skilled nursing facilities and you may find that alternate living arrangements are required as the disease progresses. ALFs are also generally not set up to provide the kind of supervision necessary for a person who wanders or has other behavioral problems.

5   Skilled nursing facilities. These are the nursing homes most people are familiar with. These provide 24-hour care and supervision, meals, and most have community activities for residents. Some nursing homes have separate Alzheimer's or dementia units. Staff in these specialized units or specialized nursing homes ideally have additional training and experience working with dementia, although facilities often fall short of this ideal. Specialized units, again ideally, are designed to prevent wandering, minimize behavioral problems, optimize the environment to let the individual operate as independently as possible, and provide levels of stimulation optimal for persons with dementia. Nursing homes are covered more fully below.

If you want to keep your loved one at home and think that you can realistically manage, there are services available to you that may help to make this possible. Even if family and friends can provide most of the caregiving, you may still occasionally need to avail yourself of additional services.

Care Alternatives

1   Home health care. Your options include hiring an independent caregiver or working through an agency. There are pros and cons to both. Hiring an independent caregiver means doing careful screening on your own— background checks, carefully checking references, credential checks are your responsibility. Issues like paying social security taxes for the employee should also be checked with a tax specialist. Unless you have back-up contingencies, you also will not have alternate care available if the individual cannot come to work. The advantage of this method is that you and the care provider determine the scope of his duties and you are not restricted to agency shift hours. Some independent caregivers may also be willing to negotiate hourly rates. Your hourly fees for caregivers from agencies may be higher as you are paying for the caregiver and agency administrative costs. Agencies may be more restrictive in terms of the duties various levels of caregivers may perform. You may also not be able to choose particular caregivers—this will vary by agency. They work shifts and you often must hire the individual for a minimum amount of time (sometimes for the whole shift). This alternative can be more expensive but may be more reliable since staff are screened by the agency. Agencies also cover staff liability, which you are responsible for if you hire independently.

2   Live-in care. Some families arrange to have a paid caregiver live with their loved one. In the long run, this may be the least costly choice when it comes to having paid caregivers tend to your loved one at home and may allow the greatest

flexibility. Live in care has the same disadvantages as hiring an independent caregiver. You must carefully screen individuals who you will have move into your house to care for a person with Alzheimer's disease.

3   Respite care. Respite care is designed to do just as its name suggests—provide relatively brief periods of respite for caregivers. If your family has one family member who is the primary caregiver, consider arranging a schedule for other capable family members to spell that individual so that he may take care of other practical matters, engage in needed leisure activities, or take brief trips. If this is not a viable alternative, there are other avenues for you to check. You may want to consider using a paid caregiver for one or two days per week—it may be a more affordable alternative than full-time care and would allow for brief, needed respite. Adult daycare centers are another alternative. Some communities have respite centers, which are designed to give caregivers a few hours of respite—they are generally open for a few hours a day and often are prepared to work with dementia patients. Community-based respite centers are often free or very low cost options. Local church and volunteer groups may also be a source for assistance and respite care.

4   Hospice. Hospice is not a building or facility but a concept of end of life care. It is typically only provided in the last few months of life. It is offered at home, in nursing homes, or in hospitals. Hospice services typically include a large range of services including but not limited to medical care by physicians and nurses, pastoral counseling, and social services. It is designed to involve the family and help the person who is dying do so with dignity and as much comfort as possible.

5   We realize you may already feel overwhelmed and do not know where to begin. Here are some places that may be able to provide information and assistance. These are listed

in the back of the book with other resources and contact information:

o   Contact your local state's agency on aging. It should be listed in your phone book. You can also find the information and some links to local agencies at the following web address: http://www.aoa.gov/aoa/pages/state.html

o   Volunteers of America may have programs in your area. Check your local phone book or the Internet.

o   Local volunteer groups and churches may have programs. Your area agency on aging should have up-to-date information about local programs. If you attend one church regularly, you may be able to instigate a program if one does not exist. There are certainly others in your community who would benefit from an organized church-affiliated volunteer service.

o   The social services department of your local hospital may be able to provide information about available services, some of which may be provided by the hospital itself.

o   Your loved one's physician may also know about local programs. Ask if she has a handout or information about local programs.

o   If you have access to the Internet, here are some resources:

- Senior resource(.com) listings of resources by state: *http://www.seniorresource.com/states.htm*
- FirstGov.gov for Seniors. The United States government web portal with federal and state resources pertinent to senior citizens listed: *http://www.firstgov.gov/Topics/Seniors.shtml*

1   Check with the above resources for community programs your loved one may be eligible for. Georgia is just one example of a state with community programs designed to help people stay at home. The Georgia Home and Community Based Services program encompasses forty-seven different services

designed to help people remain at home. Your state's department on aging should have information about available community services.

ADULT DAYCARE

The concept of adult daycare is a good one. It is designed to involve your loved one in activities and social interaction, which is geared to their level of need. While your loved one is engaged in activities throughout the day, the caregiver is free to use that time resting, running errands, engaging in needed leisure time, or what ever your needs may be.

Adult daycares are available in most communities. Some are affiliated with hospitals; others are part of community or church outreach programs. Often there is the option of having your loved one attend full or half days, five days a week or less. Some daycares specialize in dementia care, although availability of this type of daycare may be more limited.

Typically an adult daycare will have a director, a registered nurse (R.N.), a cook, and an activities director. If it is a large program it may employ several persons in these positions.

A sample day at an average Adult daycare might include:
Clients are served breakfast
An activity director will read the newspaper to the clients and discuss current events
The activity director will lead chair exercises
An arts and crafts style activity will be offered
Lunch will be served
Special entertainment, social hour or some other form of leisure activity
Clients are prepared to depart the facility

The socialization is especially important for those in the early stages. The fact that the clients are kept safe, clean, and comfortable is important for the clients in the later stages. The families of the clients often find the time away from their loved one provides enough of a respite that the loved one can remain in their home longer or perhaps for the duration of their illness.

The cost of adult daycare is something that will need to be considered. That cost is not covered by most insurance companies, but that is something that you will need to check on. You may find that this option breaks down to less out of pocket than home healthcare. Again, that depends on your specific location and the particular agencies in your area. Many adult daycares offer a sliding scale fee, which means that fees will be based on the individual's income.

HOME HEALTH OPTION

Home healthcare is a growing entity. The choice of having a caregiver come into your home can be a wonderful alternative. Your loved one will be able to remain in his familiar surroundings and you can opt for the level of care you need.

Many agencies offer the choice of a sitter, a certified nursing assistant (C.N.A), or an R.N. You will need to ask specific questions regarding the duties each would perform and the cost. It is sometimes the case that a sitter may not be authorized to toilet or bathe your loved one. Home health agencies would be listed in your yellow pages or you can consult the Social Services Department of your local hospitals.

Individuals sometimes work as caregivers for Alzheimer's patients. Again you would need to be certain what duties they are willing and able to perform. Change is never an easy thing to deal with for Alzheimer's patients, so try your best to find the right fit and be able to utilize it for as long as possible.

Take into account the hours you are most in need of help. For some agencies there will be a minimum amount of hours you must agree to.

Here are some things to consider:

1. Do I need someone with my loved one at night or during the day?
2. Will a paid caregiver prepare meals?

3. Are caregivers physically able to ambulate my loved one?
4. Do they have experience working with AD patients?
5. Do they have references?
6. Can I trust this person to be alone in my home when I am away?
7. Can I trust this person not to be abusive with someone who cannot communicate?
8. Can I afford to pay this out of pocket if it is not covered by any other source?
9. Are they willing to adjust to my schedule should my needs change?

NURSING HOME PLACEMENT

One decision that often has to be made during the middle to late stages of Alzheimer's is whether or not to move your loved one to a nursing facility. As a caregiver you will try to move heaven and earth to avoid placing your loved one in a nursing home. It isn't something you will ever forget or ever feel good about. It may, however, be your only option. Your family will have to make that decision when the time comes.

Remember that people will second-guess your decision. "We kept my husband at home. You can do it if you try." You will hear many similar opinions. You will also find many people who have made the same decision and understand what brings a family to that point. Friends, family, even relative strangers will have an opinion, and some will second-guess you no matter what decision you make. Be prepared for this eventuality and do not let it disturb you. There will always be those who think that they may have made a different decision than the one you have made. When this occurs, you may well feel increased guilt and indecisiveness. If you have made the best decision you could under *your* circumstances for *your* loved one and family, then feel as comfortable as you can with your decision. Input from professionals and those who have experience with coping with Alzheimer's disease and nursing homes can be invaluable. Seek out that input as well as information from friends and family who have first-hand knowledge about local nursing facilities, educate yourself, and make your best decision.

Once made, understand that you have done your best to take care of your loved one, yourself, and the rest of your family.

Remember, too, that no decisions in this area have to be permanent. It is best for the person with Alzheimer's disease not to be moved too frequently. Doing so is upsetting and confusing for your affected loved one. But if you have placed your family member in a nursing home and are dissatisfied with the facility, look into others and consider moving him or her. And if you have decided to try and keep your loved one at home, remember that the alternatives remain open to you. As suggested in other portions of this book, there are more avenues of assistance, such as adult daycare, than were available in the past.

Whether you have placed your loved one in a nursing facility or have been able to keep her at home, you will have to learn to advocate for your family member. This is not always an easy process. We have often learned not to question authority, particularly medical authority. Education will be your best friend in this instance. Do not be afraid to ask questions, make suggestions, and challenge any system. In the best scenario, family members, physicians, nursing home staff, and other relevant personnel work as a team. This type of working relationship ensures the best care for your loved one.

Physicians are busy and pressed for time, but they also know that working efficiently with families can ward off future problems and increased demands for time. Some facilities have teams who will work with you—the teams may include occupational and physical therapists, a social worker, a psychologist, and other professionals. All of these professionals may help to guide you through the practical and emotional processes. Ask for their help and remember, too, that you are the expert on your particular family member so contribute your knowledge to the mix.

Once the decision has been made to place someone the work begins. Choosing a nursing home is a task that cannot be taken lightly. Do not go into it blindly. Know what questions to ask and go in with them written down so that you do not forget to ask any of them.

QUESTIONS TO ASK

Ask to see the actual room that your loved one would be placed in. You may be shown a sample room that, of course, will be the best the nursing home has to offer. The room your loved one actually gets may be very different from the sample you are shown or may be in a completely different area of the nursing facility.

Ask about employee background checks. Make sure that background checks are run on all employees and contractors associated with the facility. Checks should be completed before employees begin working at the nursing home. State and federal reviews have shown that, too often, background checks are not run or completed before employees begin working. These reviews also found a surprisingly large population of people working in nursing homes who have criminal backgrounds. Your loved one will be in a vulnerable situation and you need to know that everyone who works for the facility has a clean background check. Any history of elder abuse must be registered with state agencies that license these workers, and background checks should be run through this registry as well as criminal background checks. Also ask how extensive the criminal checks are. Recent testimony in front of Congress revealed that too many nursing facilities only run checks within the state that houses the nursing facility. The background check should include the licensing registry where abuse histories are listed, state criminal background checks, and FBI criminal background checks.

Janitors, housekeepers, food service providers, CNAs, registered nurses, and other support staff will be in and out of your loved ones room and interacting with them when they are alone. It is absolutely necessary that you know they are trustworthy. The statistic on people who have shady back rounds and have found employment working with out most defenseless members of society is astounding.

Ask to see the most recent state survey. Every nursing home is subject to a state survey. A team of surveyors will come into the facility and spend several days looking at the operation. They will look through charts, observe activities, sit through meal times, interview residents and make a very detailed inspection. Their findings are compiled into a survey report and it is always available to the public. Most nursing homes keep the report in the lobby in full view. If you do not see it on display, ask for it.

It is not unusual for the survey team to find deficiencies. The important thing is the nature of the deficiency and whether or not the nursing home made the necessary corrections. For example there can be deficiencies that don't affect the direct care of the patients. Ask about any and all to be certain that you are placing your loved one in a quality facility. Keep in mind that even a nursing home with zero deficiencies can be a bad place to live. Ask residents how they like it.

You can also now read nursing home reports and compare nursing homes online through the Medicare website at *http:// www.medicare.gov.* Just click on the "nursing home compare" link to access information about specific nursing homes.

Nursing homes are a business. The size of the nursing home or the fact that it may be a chain of nursing homes does not make any real difference. Nursing homes are a business. They are in the business of making money. Don't forget that. They maintain a marketing department, which may be slick and well funded or it may be small and unimpressive. Either way, remember that nursing homes are businesses and judge them based on the fact that it is the job of the marketer to sell you on the nursing home.

Ask about turnover in staff. CNAs are the heart of the direct care staff. It will be the C.N.A. who keeps your loved one dry, safe, clean, and will attend to all of his daily needs. They are under paid and overworked. They can move from one job to the next without a second thought. Many CNAs do just that. They may not be happy with the supervision, or they may not be good at their job and have been dismissed from another facility. There is a shortage of CNAs so it is easy for them to find another position. The quality of CNS staff members varies greatly, as is true at all staff levels. Some families arrange worked with absolutely outstanding CNAs who remain friends even after the death of the individual for whom they were caring. Other aides have been less than we would hope for in someone caring for a person we love.

Your loved one will come to think of the direct care staff as family. If her "family" is constantly changing it is emotionally tough on your loved one to adjust. Your loved one needs to see familiar faces as she goes through her days and nights. A never-ending stream of new staff will only serve to upset your loved one. In some facilities the turnover is as high as seventy-five percent. Knowing that good staff could find another job at any time but choose to remain at one facility speaks volumes about the quality of the facility. Also, ask how long the administrator has been there. It is important that she has been there long enough to have full confidence in her staff.

Ask if they have Medicaid beds available. Even if you are a lottery winner, you must read this section. The cost of nursing home care can range anywhere from about $100.00 a day upwards. That does not include the cost of medicine, therapy, diapers, and many other things that will come up.

If your loved one is recuperating after having been hospitalized, Medicare may pay for a certain number of days in the nursing home. Once those days have passed or if your loved one is no longer improving those funds may be stopped.

Medicaid only kicks in once certain criteria have been met. These are very specific and you will need to investigate the rules in your particular state. Some general information is provided on Medicare and Medicaid later in this section of the book.

Alzheimer's disease can last for decades. You must be sure that the nursing home will have a bed for your loved one once your funds are depleated. Some nursing homes may maintain only a couple of Medicaid beds for a population of hundreds of residents. If that is the case, your loved one will need to be on the waiting list and hope that the time of his need for such a bed corresponds to one coming open. That is not likely to happen.

Look for a nursing home that will let your loved one's care continue uninterrupted, should you find yourself needing to apply for Medicaid. Even if that sounds like an absolute impossibility, do it anyway. The last thing you would want to do is uproot your loved one from a place he has come to think of as home and to begin your search anew.

Be sure they have a bed open. It is not always easy to find a nursing home with a bed open. It is especially hard to find one with an open bed for a male. The number of female patients far exceeds the number of males, so the turnover in placements for males is far slower.

You may find you have to place your loved one on a waiting list. If you find the perfect place, put him on the list or placement in that facility may be out of the question. You may want to have him on the waiting list at several facilities if you are fortunate enough to find more than one quality home.

Ask about wandering precautions. Your loved one must be in a facility that is adapted for those who wander. Some nursing homes have separate Alzheimer's wings with tighter security than the rest of the facility.

Additional considerations to keep in mind. Pay attention to your overall impression of the facility. Is it clean, well-lit, does it provide pleasant living conditions, are there posted announcements of activities for residents, are there programs of interest to the residents, are there liberal visiting hours? Ask to see sample menus. As one might with a child's daycare, show up unannounced to get an impression of the facility when there isn't a marketing person prepared to give you the best impression

Persons with Alzheimer's disease tend to do better in certain kinds of environments. The less cluttered nursing facility rooms are, the better. The more homelike they are, the better. Nursing homes that have common areas and bedrooms that resemble rooms you might have at home are preferable. Your loved one should be able to place personal items (e.g., photographs) around the room and not just confined them to one area, such as a bulletin board. It is better to have exits essentially hidden in the décor. While good nursing facilities will make these exits impossible for someone with

Alzheimer's to use and thus wander, you don't want people feeling like they're in jail. Facilities that design their exits so that they may be safely used by staff and others in an emergency, are preferred to facilities who's exit signs are a glaring temptation for residents. Hallways and walkways that are wide, clean, well-lit, have visual cues provided so that they are easy to navigate to a given destination, and which are not complex or confusing. The types of surroundings that have proven optimal for persons with Alzheimer's include those with moderate levels of noise and surroundings with familiar sensory experiences. Those with comforting and familiar smells, for example, are better than those that have institutional odors. A facility should have an appealing outdoor area available to persons with Alzheimer's. Some even maintain gardens that residents can participating in caring for. Again, these should be safely fenced and gated so that wandering is not possible. Ideally fencing should be unobtrusive or appealing to the eye. What would you like to see in a place where you are going to be living.

Some other considerations and questions to ask include the following:

2   Safety and access. Are there ramps and handrails outside and inside the building common areas?
3   If possible, visit unannounced during nice weather. Are residents outside enjoying the weather? Are there areas set aside so that residents with dementia can safely be outside? Are the grounds clean and well-maintained? Can residents participate in gardening?
4   When you visit, are the nursing home residents interacting with each other and socializing? Are they sitting in the hallways or are they engaged in activities?
5   Are residents allowed to provide some of their own furnishings? May your loved one's room be decorated with her own paintings and belongings?
6   Are nursing home provided furnishings clean and well-maintained?

7   Are the halls and common areas large enough, well lit, and cheerful? Are they cluttered? Are there visual cues provided so that your loved one can move around the environment as independently as possible?

8   Are there emergency evacuation plans? Are safety measures clearly taken (e.g., sprinklers, accessible fire hoses)?

9   Who provides medical care for nursing home residents? Are there non-medical clinical professionals on staff or do they visit on a regular basis? For example, does the facility have one or more physical therapists on staff? If so, how is it decided who is eligible for those services?

10   Who will give your loved one his medications and what are the supervisory requirements when it comes to medication?

11   Do residents have the opportunity to leave the facility on group trips to, for example, the local botanical garden? If so, who is available to supervise residents with dementia on those trips? Are transportation services provided if your loved one needs to see a physician? Is a staff member available to go with him if family is not able to be there? (This is particularly important when family members live in different parts of the country.)

12   Are there activities scheduled that will address your loved one's physical, mental and spiritual needs?

My Family's Experience with Nursing Home Placement

My mother was the one who had to make the ultimate decision to place dad in a nursing home. Legally it fell to her but we all agreed that we could see no other option.

Mother was initially unwavering on the issue and would not entertain the idea of placing Dad in a nursing home. She was confident that my dad would live the rest of his life at home. Mom was in her mid-seventies and her health was failing. Mom, my brothers, and I had kept vigil over My Dad for months. During those months Dad was not sleeping, he was getting upset most evenings; he was threatening to burn his car, and he was wandering away from the house. It was not a situation that could go on any longer. My mother had told us that she would know when it was time to look for a placement. What had begun as a "never" had turned into a "someday." It was soon clear that "someday" had arrived. His paranoia was making him miserable. He wasn't happy in his home—he was terrified. He wanted to "escape." My mother was having trouble separating his cruel words and actions from the disease and, as a result, she was emotionally and physically exhausted.

We went into the nursing home selection process blindly. We found a nursing home that was nearby and we made an appointment to take a tour. The lobby was lovely, as was the marketing representative "Cheryl". The room we were directed to was colorful and welcoming. The hall was quiet and peaceful. We thought we had found a wonderful place for Dad. Cheryl agreed to find a good match for a roommate and, in fact, had just the right person in mind.

The room that they had shown us was not the room in which he was placed. It wasn't even the same wing of the nursing home. On the day that he was admitted we reminded "Cheryl" the marketing person that she had promised to pair Dad up with someone he could share conversation with. Dad was instead placed in a room that looked like a hospital room. His roommate was a man in a coma. Dad had a bed and a rusty metal bedside table. There wasn't room for a chair beside his bed. We stood looking at him, shoved into the corner of the already full room, and we couldn't believe what we were seeing.

We went in search of "Cheryl," the smiling marketing person. She assured us that this was only a temporary placement. Dad would be getting a bigger room soon. We believed her.

Dad had been placed on "B" wing. "B" wing was like a scene from "Snake pit." People were screaming "help me" around the clock. Dad was aware enough to realize that he was in an awful place, but he didn't ask to go home. He never asked.

On the third day of his stay on "B" wing a nurse poured water and his medications into his mouth while he was in a deep sleep.

Fortunately my brother was standing next to the bed and as Dad began to choke, my brother sat him up.

Needless to say, we had been sold a bill of goods. The nurses were inept and the wing he was on was horrid. He was going down quickly. Dad stopped talking and just slept. He was withdrawing from the conditions all around him. We scrambled to find a better placement and this time we knew the things to look for.

We did everything right with the second nursing home. We saw the room he would be in and it was excellent. The staff was charming. The food was wonderful. Unfortunately even the best situation can change. Toward the end of Dad's second year at the nursing home the administration turned over—the nursing home was going bankrupt. The meal portions were cut down. The staff turnover was constant.

I think the lesson in all of this is keep apprised of the situation if you place your loved one in a nursing home. Be aware of changes in the quality of the care. Even a wonderful nursing home can transform.

DEMENTIA-PROOFING YOUR HOME

There are practical things that can be done to help ensure the safety of your loved one if you elect to keep him in his home. You must have the mindset of protecting them from things that they no longer understand, just as you would protect a young child. These are some of the things you can do.

1   Regulate hot water heaters to prevent scalding water.
2   If you can, replace glass in windows with Plexiglas.
3   Keep electrical appliances away from water sources.
4   Keep cabinets locked or use childproof barrier systems on your cabinets. To prevent frustration, allocate a specific cabinet for the person with Alzheimer's so that she may freely access that cabinet. Supply the cabinet with plastic cups, plates, bowls, and so on.
5   Place childproof safety plugs in empty electrical sockets.

6   Keep medications under lock and key.
7   Remove poisonous houseplants to avoid their ingestion.
8   Remove sharp objects such and knives and scissors—place them in locked cabinets or drawers.
9   Put safety covers over stove and oven range knobs so that the individual does not turn these on unbeknownst to you.
10 Keep swimming pool gates locked
11 Remove all firearms from the house.
12 Keep the noise level relatively low in your house to avoid agitation. Similarly, avoid over-stimulation in the environment.
13 Simplify your décor. A busy décor is confusing and upsetting for most people with Alzheimer's disease.
14 Remove things like glass table tops which might confuse the individual and can prove dangerous.
15 Remove throw rugs to avoid tripping. These can also create a visual cliff and confuse the individual who is walking near them.
16 Put a riser on the toilet seat to make it easier for the individual to stand back up. There are seats available that have both handrails and risers.
17 Put handrails in the bathroom by the toilet and in the bathtub/shower. Also assess hallways and stairs and make sure there is a sturdy handrail, preferably two, on all stairs the person has access to.
18 Provide orienting information. People with Alzheimer's lose sense of time—they will forget not only the current day and month, but the current year. Post a large calendar that includes the year; make sure that days are clearly marked off. Or use something like a wipe-off board to write each day in large letters the month, date, day of the week, and year. Add names to the bottoms of family pictures your loved one sees in frames around the house or in her nursing home room. This can be done simply with post-it notes. Label cupboards, drawers, and doors that your loved one uses.

19 Later in the disease, the individual may need supervision whenever he or she moves around the house. The risk of falls and serious injury increases as the disease progresses. There are various types of alarms and systems available that will alert caregivers when the individual is trying to move about the house. Systems range from using a simple baby monitor to a pressure sensitive mat placed by the bed that will sound an alarm when the individual steps on it. A list of some available alarm types and companies that sell the products is available at the following web address: http://www.alzheimersupport.com/admin/pop_funding/popfunding.cfm

Wandering Prevention and Precautions

20 Place an alarm or bell on exterior knobs to alert you if they are opened.

21 Keep doors and windows locked. Do not forget all of the doors in your house including sliding glass doors and garage doors. If one lock does not prove to be a deterrent to wandering out, try installing two locks and keep only one locked at a time. That way the individual will always be locking one lock each time the locks are manipulated. Choose locking systems that are likely to be more difficult for a person with Alzheimer's to figure out and manipulate.

22 For fire and other safety reasons, make sure all other people in the house know how to work all locking systems.

23 Inform neighbors of your loved one's illness and ask them to contact you immediately if they see your loved one leaving the house alone.

24 Inform your local police department of your loved one's illness and provide them with a recent photo in case the individual does wander away. Provide emergency contact information on the back of the photo.

25 Make sure that your loved one has identification on his or her person at all times. We recommend enrolling your loved

on in the Alzheimer's Association Safe Return Program. The program is a multifaceted one that will help to locate your loved one if he or she does wander. The program includes a number of identification methods: a bracelet or necklace, wallet cards (which should be used in combination with other methods in case the person is not carrying the wallet), and clothing labels. The program also has the following components: a national photo and information database; a 24-hour emergency crisis line; support from the local Alzheimer's Association chapter; and, education for the caregiver about wandering. The identification has the toll-free crisis line number for any individual who has found your loved one to call—the crisis line will immediately contact the people on the registered contact list. Safe Return also works with local police departments and provides them with all necessary information and a photograph should your loved one wander. The program has participated in the safe return of over six thousand Alzheimer's patients. There is a nominal fee so if you choose to forgo the program for this or other reasons, follow some of the program suggestions and make sure your loved one always has identification.

26 A device known as a Verichip has recently been implanted in one individual to test its efficacy and use. It is a tiny device implanted under the skin. A microchip contains identifying information, medical information, and emergency contact information. The chip can be read by emergency personnel and hospitals that have a scanner necessary to read the chip. This technology is very new and is not yet in widespread use, but may have valuable applications for persons with Alzheimer's and other diseases or conditions that cause a person to be unable to recall information or speak for himself.

Behavior Problems

"Behavior problems" can encompass so many different kinds of problems and causes that the term is misleadingly simple. Alzheimer's disease affects the individual's personality and cognition, and thus his or her behavior. These problems can be so wide-ranging that it is accurate to categorize them as behavior problems but is misleading for families, who often seek clearly defined solutions to "behavior problems." Whether or not you consider behaviors problems is often a matter of personal beliefs and acceptance levels, but there are certain behaviors that constitute safety problems. These would be considered problematic for most people and may indicate that the individual with Alzheimer's is in distress. These include wandering, emotional explosions, withdrawal over prolonged periods of time, pacing, and for some individuals occasional aggression (e.g., striking out).

As with all facets of Alzheimer's disease, there are no simple solutions—the behavioral difficulties caused by Alzheimer's disease have so many potential causes that solutions require trying to understand the causes of the behaviors, address the underlying causes where possible, and finding solutions that fit your situation and the individual involved. When addressing behavior problems, you must consider a triad of contributors: intrinsic factors within the individual with Alzheimer's disease, the environment, and the caregiver. Any one or all of these variables contribute to the observable reactions of a person with Alzheimer's disease.

Underlying most of the behavioral difficulties associated with Alzheimer's disease is the brain damage caused by the disease. Behavior increasingly reflects the degree of brain damage caused by the disease. When in doubt, it is safest to assume that it is the disease process that is causing behaviors that may be problematic for the individual with Alzheimer's or the caregiver.

One must also consider the person. Who the person was before developing Alzheimer's needs to be factored into all equations. For example, a person who was typically a loner but who is forced to spend a lot of time with other people in a nursing facility may react by showing signs of upset or anxiety. When that individual cannot communicate his or her distress verbally, it will be exhibited in sometimes disruptive behavior. Finding a way for the individual to safely spend some time alone may help to alleviate part of the problem and takes into consideration who the person is as an individual.

Understanding how to deal with problematic behaviors means understanding what precipitates the behaviors. The best way to deal with issues of behavior is to prevent the behaviors. To do this, there are a number of issues to consider and attend to:

1   Take into consideration who the individual was before the disease complicated existing personality and coping styles. A person who was previously uncomfortable with being nude in front of other people, for example, may become agitated when others try to assist with bathing. Finding ways to make the process more comfortable for the individual (e.g., only one or two family members who the person may be more comfortable with bathing the individual; using towels and other methods to protect as much of his or her privacy as possible) may help, as will your empathy.

2   Make sure the person is not experiencing a physical problem. Some physical causes of acting out behaviors include fever, medication interactions or side effects, pain, illness, and the need to void.

3   Pay attention to the process. Are there things that you can pinpoint that precede episodes of pacing, wandering, aggression, and other behaviors? In an individual who does not have the cognitive capacity to identify and/or communicate distress will show it through behavior.

4   As objectively as possible, look at your role in the individual's
     distress. Are there things that you do that may contribute
     to precipitating the behaviors? People with dementias are
     often very sensitive to nonverbal communications as well as
     to criticism, feeling infantalized, being pushed past their
     capacities, nonverbally communicating frustration or anger,
     and so on. Honest introspection and analysis of the process
     can help you to identify things that you can change in your
     interactions. The individual with Alzheimer's isn't able to
     engage in this kind of process, so it is up to people without
     cognitive challenges to do so.

5   Assess the physical environment and how the individual
     reacts to different aspects of the environment. Environment
     is discussed more fully in the section dealing with dementia-
     proofing the home. It can have a significant impact on the
     person's sense of safety and well-being, and thus on behavior.
     Environment includes variables such as numbers of people
     in a room at any given time, lighting, clutter, and so on.
     Observe the individual's behavior for clues to environmental
     influences on his or her behavior. Too many people or too
     much stimulation in the environment will cause confusion
     and subsequent behavioral reactions.

6   Both overstimulation and boredom can cause problem
     behaviors. Wandering, pacing, withdrawal, and other
     behaviors may be associated with environments that are
     overwhelming to the individual. Paradoxically, boredom may
     cause the same behaviors. People with dementing conditions
     require stimulation but cannot be overwhelmed with it.
     Finding a balance between too much stimulation and
     maintaining an environment that is stimulating enough is
     key. To do this, take into consideration safety issues, the
     individual's past interests, likes and dislikes, and be sensitive
     to changes in behavior to gauge where the line resides for
     your loved one. Research has repeatedly shown that ideal
     environments for persons with dementia provide cognitive
     stimulation tailored to capitalize on individual strengths

and compensate for deficits; provides moderate physical exercise within the person's capabilities; and meets the emotional needs of the individual by being age-appropriate, providing positive rewards, being as stress-free as possible, and supports the individual's sense of being a worthwhile person.

7   Has the individual been overtaxed with expectations? Tasks that you think the individual is able to accomplish may be too difficult and frustrating. It is important to let the person do as much for himself or herself as possible, but also to assist the individual when necessary. Remember that the ability to perform one task does not mean that another similar task can be successfully accomplished, or that a task that was completed one time can be completed the next time. Skill level will fluctuate and varies across different abilities. Overlearned tasks may be easier for the individual to successfully undertake, but most things we do require multiple steps. The individual may not be able to sequence and plan sufficiently to work through all of the steps, and so will need tasks broken down to manageable small steps.

8   Is the individual experiencing excess disability? Excess disability (Kahn, 1975) means that the person is disabled beyond the level caused by Alzheimer's. Hearing problems, visual deficits, medication side effects or interactions, environmental stressors, and treatable psychiatric symptoms can contribute to the person functioning below the level that is caused by the dementia itself. These factors and the excess disability caused by them can cause behavioral problems that may be alleviated by treating disabilities that are treatable (e.g., using hearing aids and wearing appropriate lenses to correct vision).

9   Learn to prioritize. Behaviors that indicate unease in the person with Alzheimer's need to be addressed, as do those that pose risk to safety and well-being. Many behaviors can be irritating, such as the tendency to ask the same questions over and over, but they are not a threat to anyone and can be relatively easily accommodated. Decide which behaviors

are merely irritating but really do not pose a serious problem for anyone or signify a real problem with your loved one, and then shrug those behaviors off. This does not mean ignore the person when he or she engages in behaviors you find irritating—doing so will only cause upset and intensify the behaviors—it means shrug off your irritation and realize that the only thing you likely can change under the circumstances is your reaction. In essence, learn to choose your battles.

Caregivers who have dealt with similar problems may be able to offer assistance when they have found solutions that work for them. Their solutions to specific problems may or may not work for your loved one. The advice we offer here is more generalized with the goal of prevention and being able to encourage an approach that will lead to flexibility in the way that you approach problems and solutions that will generalize across many different kinds of situations, not specific problems. Even optimal situations, though, are not likely to prevent all problems. Alzheimer's leads people to be unpredictable and inconsistent, requiring flexibility on the part of caregivers. Some of the problems that may arise despite your best efforts are discussed below.

Driving

Driving eventually becomes a problem for everyone with Alzheimer's. How long your loved one can drive will have to be judged and evaluated by family members who witness driving behavior, physicians, and possibly the motor vehicle department. Driving becomes a bone of contention for many families. We relish our independence and in the United States, that often means driving. If your loved one becomes unsafe behind the wheel and refuses to give up driving, you will have to force the issue. Some families hide keys and disable cars by simple means that can be easily reversed. Sometimes, it is necessary to go further. You can contact your local department of motor vehicles and discuss how to revoke the license of a person who is impaired. To remove family members from the fray, your loved one's physician(s) can also report an individual as being unable to drive due to cognitive or other impairments.

Below is a table reprinted with permission of the Hartford Financial Services group. It provides some guidelines for considering whether it is time for the person with dementia to relinquish driving privileges:

Early Warning Signs of Driving Problems:

- Incorrect signaling
- Trouble navigating turns
- Moving into a wrong lane
- Confusion at exits
- Parking inappropriately
- Hitting curbs
- Driving at inappropriate speeds
- Delayed responses to unexpected situations
- Not anticipating dangerous situations
- Increased agitation or irritation when driving
- Scrapes or dents on car, garage or mailbox
- Getting lost in familiar places
- Near misses
- Ticketed moving violations or warnings
- Car accident
- Confusing brake for gas pedals
- Stopping in traffic for no apparent reason

Catastrophic Reactions and Aggressive Behavior

Catastrophic reactions are overreactions to stress, often quite minor stress. These reactions can include angry outbursts, weeping, pacing, trying to leave the house, and sometimes aggressive behaviors. These are not the willful or childish response of an intact adult; they are a response guided by brain damage. Inability to control behavior coupled with the individual's inability to assess a problem and work through the problem contribute to catastrophic reactions.

As with all behavioral problems, it is best to try to prevent these reactions by eliminating conditions that lead to them. Preventing the reactions means learning to know what triggers upset in your loved one and avoiding the triggers, as well as learning the early warning signs of upset and trying to defuse the situation before it escalates. The conditions are the same discussed under the general category of "Problem Behaviors." If a catastrophic reaction occurs, it is important to:

1   Remain calm and reassuring. Try to look past the behavior itself to understand what caused the behavior. Remember that the individual is not able to control his or her behavior at this point so it is up to you to defuse the situation. Keep your voice level, calm, and soothing. If you overreact, you will cause the problem behavior(s) to escalate.

2   Do not overwhelm the person with too many choices. A person with Alzheimer's has difficulty making even the simplest decisions under the best of circumstances, and cannot do so when agitated. Calmly direct the person rather than making a request or offering a choice.

3   When you can identify an environmental trigger for the catastrophic reaction, address the issue by either removing a distressing person or object.

4   Even if you cannot understand what has upset the individual, try to empathize with the underlying emotions without being condescending.

5   Maintain routines. Interruption of routines and lack of predictability in the environment is upsetting to a person with Alzheimer's disease.

6   Do not argue or try to reason with the individual. This will only cause further upset. Remember, the individual is at a significant disadvantage when it comes to arguing and the inability to put his or her distress into words and, further, to engage in an argument will only cause the situation to escalate.

7   Negative reactions, such as chiding the individual, are only likely to make the situation worse. Use positive reinforcement

to divert the individual, including smiling, hugs if he or she is not too agitated to have you approach and embrace or provide gentle pats, divert by offering positive reinforcers rather than threatening with negative ones.

8   Do not try to physically restrain the individual. This will only engender fear and may lead to the person striking out.

9   Distraction frequently works. Try to distract the individual from focusing on his or her distress. Pick an activity that the person typically finds pleasurable.

10 Reassure. The individual may be frightened or anxious about something you cannot identify. Regardless of what you think the cause may be, reassure the individual that he or she is safe.

11 Be creative and keep track of what works and what does not. Make sure that all people caring for your loved one are consistent and follow guidelines that have proven effective.

12 Keep an open mind. You may find that others have creative solutions to problems that stymie you. This is a team effort, one that requires all of your patience, common sense, and creativity.

Sexually Inappropriate Behavior

People with Alzheimer's disease will sometimes act in sexually inappropriate ways. Sexually inappropriate behaviors may include exposing private parts, making inappropriate sexual advances, groping, and exhibiting paranoia about the sexual acts of others, which may lead to false accusations.

Like other Alzheimer's behaviors, this can have a number of causes. Some of the causes can be disinhibition due to specific kinds of brain damage, the need to void, failure to recognize people who one should not approach in a sexual way, misreading environmental cues (i.e., erroneously thinking that a sexual invitation has been proffered), and other cognitive slippages due to the disease process.

Here, as in so many areas, you must learn to pick your battles. As with other problematic behaviors, try to understand the cause of the behavior by attending to triggers or the process by which the person begins to engage in the objectionable behavior. Once you have identified the correct cause(s), it is easier to avoid the behavior altogether. If you have not been able to avoid the behavior, redirect the individual when he or she begins to engage in the behavior. Do not belittle or reprimand the person—it is unlikely the individual is aware that he or she is being inappropriate and reprimanding the behavior will only cause upset and make the situation worse.

Foul language may be quite objectionable to some people, particularly if there are children in the environment. It may be less offensive to others who can easily ignore the language. In either case, some people with Alzheimer's use foul language, particularly if they used it prior to developing the disease. It may be unavoidable. Unless the individual is exposing himself or herself or is being sexually aggressive, it is best to ignore as much of the behavior as possible. Distract or redirect the person when the behavior becomes inappropriate.

General Tips and Guidelines

In all situations, there are some guidelines you should keep in mind.

1   The person with Alzheimer's is most likely trying his or her best. No one wants to be incompetent or look incompetent—this is not willful behavior. When in doubt, assume that behaviors you do not understand are caused by the disease, not the individual acting voluntarily.

2   Do not overtax capabilities. Break tasks down into manageable small steps and assist as necessary. Find a balance between helping and encouraging the individual to do as much as possible independently. Capitalize on the person's remaining capabilities and help him compensate for his deficits.

3   Do not infantalize the person. People with Alzheimer's want to be viewed as most adults do, as capable, worthwhile individuals. Maintaining one's pride and dignity are as important now as they ever were, perhaps more.

4   Do not criticize or belittle. Positive reinforcement is the most effective way of encouraging the person and directing behavior. Criticism will only make the individual feel inept and stupid, and may well precipitate a catastrophic reaction. When guiding behavior, tell the person what to do, avoid telling him or her what *not* to do. As suggested in the section on communication, use simple, appropriate communication styles.

5   Try to provide an environment that stimulates enough to avoid boredom but, at the same time, does not overstimulate the person. Where the difference falls will depend on the individual with Alzheimer's disease.

6   Include the individual as much as possible in family activities. It is lonely to feel left out. When it is impossible to include the individual, find alternatives that may be equally or almost equally pleasurable for the individual.

7   Maintain your sense of humor and remember that the person with Alzheimer's also needs laughter in his or her life.

8   Finally, remain flexible. Alzheimer's disease leads to unpredictable behaviors, fluctuations in abilities and behaviors, and changes as the disease progresses. Your ability to remain flexible will enable you to meet the demands of the situation as it changes over time.

References:

Kahn, R. L. (1975). The mental health system and the future aged. *The Gerontologist, 15*, 24-31.

Communication,
the challenges and the gifts

The give and take of good conversation is a joy. We can be introduced to a total stranger and develop a friendship within minutes if the conversation is open and honest. The friendships formed through the writing of this book were cemented before we ever met. Merely through the process of the writing and with communication that doesn't require a face to face encounter. When your loved one becomes ill with a disease such as Alzheimer's one of the first things you may notice is a change in his or her ability to communicate.

In the earliest stages of Alzheimer's disease you may notice afflicted people searching for the right word. The halting speech pattern and word searching may not raise a red flag at first. Everyone has occasionally forgotten the word they are looking for or lost their train of thought. This is frustrating when it happens to us. We *know* what we want to say but can't get to it. It is even more frustrating when this becomes an ever-increasing occurrence and an indication of more than a fleeting problem.

You may hear people with relatively early Alzheimer's say things such as, "I needed to go to the . . . . oh, you know . . . . the place where I buy food." The word "store" has slipped from their minds and trying to retrieve it may become too much for them, so they give you hints like "the place where I buy food." This kind of halting communication may seem tiresome, but if you remember that even this form of communication will eventually become very rare you will learn to cherish these conversations.

Early in the disease, it is words that are used infrequently that are lost, as are the names of people who are seen or talked about only occasionally. As time progresses, commonly used words and the names of people closest to the individual will also be lost.

One way that the Alzheimer's patient tries to cope with this lack of word finding is to cover. Covering is a term to describe the means people find to keep others unaware of their difficulties with speaking and remembering. Others may try to isolate themselves in order to avoid the challenge of communicating once they realize there is a problem. Some people laugh off an incident as a temporary aberrance, even though the person may be aware that it is happening more and more frequently.

Another way in which a person may try to cover for memory lapses is to call friends and family members by a generic term such as "pal" or "sweetie," or some other term of endearment. If this generic naming gives them a sense of comfort then let it be. The biggest mistake you can make is to put them on the spot by quizzing them on names and facts. Below are some other communication hints and techniques:

1   Look the individual in the eye when speaking to her.
2   Remember that people with Alzheimer's are very sensitive to your nonverbal communications and may become agitated if you show irritation, anger, frustration, and similar emotions. Keep your voice warm, calm, and friendly.
3   Keep it simple. Avoid complex sentences and complex grammatical structure. For example: DON'T ASK: "Would you like to wear your blue sweater or your green sweater?" DO ASK: "Would you like to wear your blue sweater?" If the individual says no, offer the green sweater in a separate question.
4   When possible, avoid even asking the question and just make a simple statement. "Here is your blue sweater." When dealing with something that the person dislikes, such as dressing if this is an issue for your loved one, do not offer options just make a simple statement. "Time to get dressed."
5   Always remember to speak to the person respectfully. No one likes to be condescended to, including people with Alzheimer's disease.

6   Cover only one topic at a time. Talking about more than one subject is too confusing and will leave the person with Alzheimer's confused.

7   Be very specific when you talk. Avoid using nondistinct words, including pronouns. For example: "They're going to the beach," is too confusing. "Susan and Fred are going to the beach" is more likely to be understood.

8   Pick your times to discuss important issues. Usually early in the day is best for a person with Alzheimer's disease. Do not discuss important issues when the individual is tired, which is usually later in the day.

9   Patience. Give the person time when he is trying to express himself. Do not rush to finish his sentences or guess at the word he is trying to find. Do not brush off an unfinished thought and move on to something else. Give the person time to put the words together if he can. You will look back on these times of stammering speech with longing, so don't be too impatient to move ahead too fast.

10 Do not put the person with Alzheimer's on the spot. Do *not,* for example, say "Do you remember when we . . . ." Instead, help jog the person's memory: "I remember when we . . . ."

11 In later stages when communication may be nonexistent, keep talking to the person even if she cannot talk back. And a warm smile and loving touch do as much or more to communicate love as verbal communications.

As people begin to lose the ability to express themselves you may find them becoming depressed. Something is wrong with their minds and they may be noticing it, now they have the added problem of not being able to explain what they are thinking or feeling. As a psychological defense they may be angry or accuse you of not listening. They may deny having been told things that they cannot remember. If you are not aware of their illness these accusations and their anger can seem to come out of the blue. Do not argue these issues—doing so will only frustrate and embarrass the individual. Let it go and, if it helps, blame yourself rather than the person with Alzheimer's: "Maybe I forgot to tell you. I'm sorry." It is far more important to consider the psychological well-being of the person at these times than to argue the little issues.

Above all it is important that you try to keep your frustration in check. As a caregiver you already have huge concerns about the future. No doubt ever since the diagnosis you are left wondering what will become of your loved one and, indeed, what will become of you. These fears and worries are to be expected and certainly deserve attention. Unfortunately your loved one is not the person you should share these concerns with. She is in the vortex of this and cannot help you. There are those who can— friends, your church, and both informal and formal support groups. If it is your spouse who has Alzheimer's, the most natural thing in the world though will be to turn to your partner and vent. Don't do it. Resist at all costs. Your spouse with Alzheimer's just can't help you, and to try to get him to will only make you feel dismissed.

"I can't even talk to him anymore. He just doesn't care about what I am going through." If you are measuring your loved one's ability to "care" based on his or her healthy body and mind, you may say these words: caring requires understanding on their part. Caring requires being able to put themselves in your place. It requires cognitive integration of incoming and outgoing messages. The person no longer has these capabilities. The brain controls our emotions as well as cognition and motor behavior. Perhaps one of the hardest things to accept is the fact that even though your loved one looks "normal," his or her brain is changing. This is an organic reality, not an attitude.

As the disease progresses communication deteriorates on the part of the person with Alzheimer's. You often find yourself straining to understand what has been said. This is particularly frustrating when it is clear that the individual is upset about something—it is often difficult to put your finger on the source of the distress and the exact nature of the emotion, which are sometimes clear and sometimes baffling.

At these times it can be very effective to cut through the content and pay attention to the process of what someone with Alzheimer's (and other conditions with impaired communication) says. They're often communicating the emotion pretty effectively, even if the specific content of the communications makes no sense. While the communications may appear garbled and nonsensical at times, you can cut through the apparently meaningless content by paying attention to the emotions your loved one is trying to convey. "She left me at school and I didn't have any way of getting home," may appear to be a confused communication where your loved one is regressing to childhood and speaking about a mother or other caregiver. While that may be true cognitively, what is happening emotionally and what is the thought communicating? Pay attention to the emotions and the nonverbal information conveyed—is your loved one afraid? Lonely? Sad? Feeling particularly lost or abandoned? If you attend to the context of the communications you may also pick up important clues. What led up to the communication? Put yourself in the shoes of the person with Alzheimer's to try and understand his or her reaction.

Empathize with the emotional content of the communications even if you have not understood the content. Pay attention to nonverbal as well as verbal behaviors and you will be able to deduce with a great deal of accuracy what the person is feeling.

Focusing on the emotional content also sometimes provides a sufficient distraction. Sometimes, once the person has made the emotional connection, the specific communication is forgotten and the person is satisfied. It doesn't always work, but does enough so that it is worth trying each time you are at a loss to understand the content of conversations.

We often don't remember how complicated speech is and what a complex series of neurological events it requires. Even initiating a sentence can be difficult for someone with Alzheimer's—initiation is a problem in general. Speech, initiating it, and all of the complicated aspects of adult communication depend on several areas of the brain being intact. With an otherwise healthy brain, we can sometimes compensate if one small area important for speech has a small, circumscribed lesion. The Alzheimer's brain has too much global damage for compensation to work as the disease progresses. Given the degree that speech is impacted fairly early on, it is a lot to ask later in the disease for someone to put together comprehensible speech. At times, the best he will be able to do is repeat something another person has just said (echolalia), sometimes over and over (perseveration) until you think you will scream. Remember that this is the best the person can manage. He is reaching out to you without having the communication skills we are used to. If you can, reframe your perception of what communication "should be" and learn to accept what communication the person with Alzheimer's has to offer—it is all that person has, and all too soon even that will be gone.

Even a one sided conversation can be a rewarding thing if you are communicating with your heart. Tell the person the things that you want her to know, the things that will make her feel loved and safe. Relive your happier moments out loud. Paint a word picture of the moments of your life that were special to you together. You are now the keeper of these memories; share them as stories with the one you love.

There are experts who could tell you in terms most of us do not understand why the human brain is unable to pull up those memories and phrases and names that mean so much to us as caregivers. We ache to hear them say our name or tell us that we are loved. The fact that there is an organic and specific reason why those precious abilities are no longer there will not take away the pain. It does help if you can accept that the brain is an organ that can shut down just as our kidneys can shut down. It is not a willful withdrawal from reality. It is rather a form of brain damage that is cruel in its taking of the things we hold most dear.

There are a lot of good resources out there for helping you discuss the past. Many magazines are full of articles and photographs of things from the past. Your family photo album and films are good sources of conversation. Again, do not quiz your loved one by asking; "do you know who that is?" Just point to a picture and make a comment about it. Say something like "doesn't sis look cute in that dress?" That way the individual with Alzheimer's is already given the name of the person, but in a way that would not embarrass her.

Do not make the mistake of just talking about the past, though. Your loved one needs to talk. Some people are more accustomed to talking about themselves and their feelings than others. A person with Alzheimer's or any other disease, regardless of past history of talking about feelings, needs to know that the floor is open to them and they are free to talk about anything, including their feelings about Alzheimer's and other pertinent issues. Talk about the present and the future, as well as the past. And remember, having a disease does not mean that it is the *only* thing that people want to talk about—politics, sports, card games . . . . any subject that was of interest to your loved one in the past should still be topics for discussion. And do not omit humor and laughter!

We are aware of the fact that we refer to Alzheimer's patients as "them." It bothers us to even write that word. The problem is they are "them" in the sense that they are not sharing the same reality as you. They may believe that they are living in a different decade, a different part of the world; they are in a different place in their minds when they are in the later stages. If you can respect that and validate the things they tell you, they will feel comfortable talking with you.

Validation therapy was conceived beginning in the 1960s and has recently received more attention. Although there are not many studies that look at the efficacy of validation therapy and those few studies that have been run have been quite small (thus yielding results that need to be replicated in larger populations before they can generalize to large groups of people), anecdotal reports about the efficacy of validation have been generally positive. It is basically the idea of joining the individual in his or her reality, rather than correcting the person and trying to force the individual into our reality.

Time is a jumble for people with Alzheimer's disease—the past, present, and future are intermixed in a way that is confusing for the person with the disease and for caregivers. The reality of someone with Alzheimer's is foreign to those of us without the disease, but it is their current reality. Meeting them in their place rather than trying to force them into ours often works to improve communication, self-esteem, feelings of peacefulness and safety, harmony, and so on. One caution: choose the times when you engage in validation. Do *not* validate paranoid ideation, such as often occurs when the individual believes people are stealing or plotting against him or her. In that case, empathize with the individual's feelings, reassure the individual that he or she is safe, and, if possible, redirect by engaging the person in a pleasurable activity. Use your common sense and you will find pleasant times to join with your loved one in his or her world.

By letting your loved ones feel that they can talk to you and not be challenged about the content of their communications, you will keep the lines of communication open for as long as possible. And when the individual with Alzheimer's can no longer hold up her end of a conversation, you can communicate safety, love, and respect through your words, your actions, and your loving touch.

JOURNALLING

When my dad experienced his first "episode" I started keeping a journal. I would make a quick note about what was going on, good and bad. I also found that writing poems, something I was already doing, helped me deal with my emotions.

Keeping the journal also helped me keep track of things like his tests, doctors appointments, medications, and how the disease was affecting him. Looking back I can read page after page and see how he was descending into the rabbit hole, as in Alice in Wonderland, and realize that everything that could be done was done.

My father's illness didn't happen in a vacuum. Even during the most emotionally and physically draining days we were also attending to my husband's mother. She was dying. After helping her with her daily needs for over ten years, after her husband's death, she could no longer live at home. She had signed herself into a nursing home and her body was shutting down. With two people in the family facing life-threatening illnesses the journal became a necessity. I could refer to it in order to stay organized and, most importantly, to express my feelings. Bottling up our emotions only makes them build. Obviously you cannot let fly all of the anxiety and heartbreak to those who are the source of these feelings. I couldn't tell Dad that I was eaten up inside with sorrow and worried about his future. I couldn't tell him or my mother-in-law about the toll all of the stress was taking, but I could write about it. The process of doing that released the pent up emotions. It was a healthy release.

It is common for caregivers to note that they, too, are having memory problems. This comes out of the constant stress and strain of dealing with the ever-changing situation. For some, it may also be the ramification of clinically significant depression and/or anxiety. 'Keeping a journal will be a good way to help yourself remember up coming events and it will help you have a place to write down your innermost feelings.

Venting will become a necessity. Whether you have another person you can vent to or you use your journal to let it all out, you must have a release. Dr. Patricia Stark, a noted psychologist, suggests that by journaling you can deal with the "unfinished business" of life when someone you love becomes ill. It is natural to feel that a "contract has been broken," that contract being that they would remain a part of your life. This is especially true for spouses of Alzheimer's patients.

I would also recommend that you give a brief (or very extensive) summary of what is going on with your loved one. You may want to refer back at some point, especially if you make a change in doctors or placement. You would be surprised how tough it is to keep the facts straight when your head is full of problems.

A journal will help you remember the good moments with your loved one. I remember going for a walk with my dad just after his diagnosis. He was still able to remember most things but would have trouble getting the words out. I asked him "Who was the first girl you ever kissed?"

I saw a twinkle in his eyes and a hint of a blush as he thought back.

"My first kiss was with a pretty little girl who lived down the street from me. We were both little kids."

If I hadn't known that my dad was losing his memory I wouldn't have ever asked him that question. If I hadn't written it down I might have forgotten about his answer. My journal is full of things that I learned about his life. Now that his memory is so impaired I tell HIM about his life. He listens as if I am telling him a great story that he has never heard. I tell him about his father and the things that they did together. My mother, my siblings and I are the keeper of my dad's life story. It doesn't have to die with him.

It is too late now for my father to tell me more about himself, but I have listed some things that I wish I had asked. Perhaps you can ask them of your loved one. I'm sure you will think of so many more questions. Remember to write their responses down in your journal.

1. What is your first memory?
2. What was your favorite subject in school?
3. Tell me about your favorite teacher?
4. What were you like as a little boy (or girl)?
5. Who were your best friends?
6. Did you live in the same house all of your childhood?
7. Did you ever have a dog? Tell me about it.
8. What did you want to be when you were little?
9. Who were your heroes?
10. What were you afraid of?
11. What was your proudest moment?
12. Tell me about the day I was born?
13. What was your first job?
14. What was your first car?
15. Where is the most beautiful place you have ever been?

16. What is your biggest regret?
17. What is your biggest accomplishment?
18. What do your want us to remember about you?
19. Tell me about the best Christmas of your life?
20. Tell me about your wedding day?
21. Do you want to talk about Alzheimer's? I'm here for you.

Your journal will be a gift to you. It will help your transition through the months and years that lie ahead. It will help you see the personal growth that comes out of loss. It will help you get to the feelings that are building inside of you out into the open where you can deal with them. There are no rules, no minimum number of sentences you must write or pages you must fill. Write when you wish, spill your feelings out unbridled to an audience of understanding human beings. Write letters to your loved one as if they could understand every word. Write letters to God if you wish. When you finish your writing you may want to keep it, and it is good to look back at it, or you may want to destroy it. You will know.

Essential Information for

Navigating the Mist

The Stages Of Alzheimer's Disease

Physicians and researchers use different schemes for conceptualizing Alzheimer's in stages. The most commonly used in American clinical practice is a three-stage model, which we've chosen to use here. You will find that it is difficult to pigeonhole your loved one into any specific stage—one day he may seem to be in stage two and the next in stage one. Staging is provided to give a rough guideline and help you understand what to expect with the passage of time.

EARLY STAGES

In the earliest stages of Alzheimer's disease you may notice only the slightest changes in your loved one. They may complain of feeling tired or seem unmotivated. They may appear to be forgetting things more often. They may tell you something several times in the same day or call you to tell you something they have already told you. Items will likely be misplaced and may later be found in strange places, such as one's car keys in the freezer. While we all misplace things occasionally, these events tend to occur more and more frequently. Early changes may be so subtle they may only be seen in hindsight.

There are misconceptions about the changes that occur in memory and other cognitive functions as we age. The kinds of memory changes that signal the presence of a problem are beyond those seen in normal aging. Our memories do change as we age, but in reality memory deteriorates very little and the changes do not impact ability to function normally. The changes that begin to be seen even early in Alzheimer's disease begin to affect the individual's ability to function normally. While an occasional slip is normal, in early stages of Alzheimer's, memory slips begin to occur more and more frequently and impact daily living.

As the disease progresses they may have problems remembering the day of the week or even the month and year. Telling time may begin to be a challenge. It is helpful to keep a memo board with the day of the week, day of the month, the month, and the year written on it. It will help them to stay oriented and they won't be embarrassed by having to ask. You can also use the memo board to remind them of things they will be doing in the near future. These visual cues are very helpful for them in the early stages. The term for this kind of forgetting is disorientation.

The individual may also become disoriented in space and can become lost in familiar surroundings. If you notice her becoming disoriented, take precautions to insure she doesn't get lost. It is better to err on the side of caution than to risk her wandering off.

If your loved one is used to taking walks alone you might ask to join him. If you do so in a way that doesn't lead him to believe you don't trust his ability to do it alone, he will probably welcome the company. The conversations you can have during these times together in the early stages of the disease will be among the memories you will treasure.

Apraxia is a term that refers to forgetting how to perform complex actions. We say complex, but something as simple as how to blow out a match or wave goodbye can be forgotten. Apraxia and other cognitive deficits will lead the person to forget how to use tools, utensils, and other familiar objects. A carpenter may forget which end of the screwdriver to use. A toothbrush may be mistaken for a comb. Devices they have used everyday of their lives are suddenly foreign. Simplify their worlds as much as you can, and if they do make a mistake with a tool, gently assist them or overlook it if it is safe to do so. Do what you can to help them maintain their dignity and spare them embarrassment.

Do you know that feeling when you forget what you were going to say? It is there one moment and gone the next? It is irritating to have the word on the tip of your tongue and not be able to remember it. Imagine feeling like that over and over throughout the day, day after day. The medical word for that is anomia. You will notice this increasing as the disease progresses. Be in tune with your loved ones. They will send you signals about whether they want your help in thinking of the word or if they would rather not have attention drawn to their problem. It is important that you not show dissatisfaction toward them when this occurs. They are already full of feelings of frustration.

You may see changes in personality, moods, and behavior. They may appear not to care about your feelings. They may behave in a way that seems selfish or agitated. A person who is normally upbeat may seem depressed. These changes are due to the disease and are not behavioral choices. They are at the mercy of something that has a hold of them—it is the Alzheimer's that is changing their behavior. It is absolutely necessary that you come to terms with that fact. Your loved ones with Alzheimer's are as distressed about the changes as you are, and are unable to do anything to stop the inexorable progression of Alzheimer's.

Sometimes the afflicted person may behave in a childish manner, sulking or pouting. She may say things that hurt your feelings or make accusations. It is common for someone with Alzheimer's to begin to question a spouse and ask if they are married. They may say that they want a divorce or believe that the spouse is not their spouse. These deeds are unsettling for the caregiver, but if they understand that it is a part of the illness and if they are prepared for these changes it will make the situations easier to deal with. Do what you can to put the afflicted person's fears to rest. Understand that he no longer has the ability to take in the facts and recall them. For example, if he is asking the whereabouts of a person who is no longer living and you explain that the person has died it will often times be an emotional blow to them as if learning for the first time of the death. If he continues to ask for that person and each time is told the person is dead, he will grieve the loss over and over. He cannot retain the fact that the person is dead. If possible it is best to say something to the effect of "they are not here right now" then move on to another subject.

There are medications that can alleviate much of the anxiety and agitation that your loved one is experiencing. Be open and honest with her doctors and let them know that these behavior changes are occurring. The doctors can only help your loved one as much as you allow. The more information you give them, the better the results will be.

There are also changes in what professionals call "executive functions." Judgment and reasoning, abstract thinking, ability to plan out even a simple task like making a sandwich, and loss of initiative may all occur early in the disease. Because of poor or altered judgment, the individual may begin to have problems handling money and other functions involving judgment. They are particularly vulnerable to telemarketers and other businesses that prey on people with vulnerabilities. The individual will appear to think more concretely—ability to think about problems and situations at his normal level of abstraction decreases. He may seem to have little initiative to do anything—someone who was active and engaged in life then seems to withdraw and lead an unusually passive life.

THE MIDDLE STAGES

Commonly, most of the time that your loved one lives with Alzheimer's disease will be spent in the middle stages. It is in the middle stages that the most dramatic changes will occur. Personality changes become more pronounced, as does cognitive decline. During this stages, people with Alzheimer's may become suspicious of people around them and may hide things that they fear will be stolen. It is common for someone with Alzheimer's disease to spend the day hiding car keys, purses, wallets, and other personal items, only to later search for them for hours. This behavior may repeat itself throughout the illness. Mail may be hidden. Money may be concealed and the Alzheimer's patient will become very upset when he can no longer remember where items have been placed. Oftentimes they may not remember having hidden it and they may accuse those around them of having stolen their possessions.

Care must be taken to insure that someone in the middle stages of Alzheimer's is not taken advantage of by those who would use their lack of memory and cognitive skills to swindle them. Someone who is trusted must take over the financial obligations of the Alzheimer's patient—handing bills and other financial matters becomes impossible for the person with this disease.

Alzheimer's patients often have perceptual problems. They may perceive a change in the color of carpeting or flooring as a hole that they must step over or step around. They my attempt to pick flowers on wallpaper or fabrics; these pictures or patterns may appear to be three dimensional to the Alzheimer's patient. Repetitive gestures or movements occur in the middle stages. Many patients' will scratch at a mark on a tabletop or fold napkins into tiny squares. When you see these repetitive movements understand that it is a common behavior called "perseveration."

The risk of falls increases in the middle stages as the Alzheimer's afflicted person has more problems with balance. These perceptual-motor problems may make it necessary for the Alzheimer's patient be assisted with walking and transferring in and out of bed and chairs.

Many Alzheimer's patients will persist in thinking that they are supposed to be at work. They may become verbally abusive with those who try to explain that they no longer hold a job. An Alzheimer's patient sometimes believes he has left a child at home alone and may become emotional as he insists the child needs him.

Some Alzheimer's patients experience hallucinations. They may engage in conversation with people or animals that are not real. They may believe that the person they are "seeing" is a threat to them. They may "hear" things that are not reality based. They may believe someone is talking about harming them or someone they love.

Sundowning is a term used to describe the phenomenon of increased restlessness and irritability, sometimes with hallucinations, in the afternoon and evening. Again, this is a common behavior. The reason for sundowning is not known. It should be brought to the attention of the individual's physician, who may consider medications to help decrease the phenomenon.

At some point in the illness you will notice the Alzheimer's patient is unable to recall the names of persons, perhaps even the names of family members. She may recall distant memories more readily than recent events. These two types of memories are stored in different parts of the brain. The most recent memories are the first to fade, and memories of the distant past may be retained when most or all ability to recall recent events is gone.

As the Alzheimer's patient moves through the middle stages they will loose the ability to carry on a conversation. They will have difficulty keeping the thread of the conversation. As the person moves nearer the final stage of the disease there will be more erosion of their ability to communicate.

Loss of bowel and bladder control is common in the middle stages. It is imperative that they be kept dry and clean in order to prevent skin breakdowns.

During the middle stages of the disease it is necessary to have the Alzheimer's afflicted person supervised at all times. He is no longer able to make safe choices regarding the daily routine. Provisions should be made to insure the person is eating nutritious meals but not preparing them. He should not be left on his own allowing opportunity for him to wander and become lost. The caregiving team should be well into the routine of providing a safe environment for the ever-increasing needs of the patient.

The middle stages are difficult for the patient and the caregiver. The situation is fluid and, just as you think you have solved a problem, a new one will present itself. Stay positive and utilize any and all resources available.

Medicare Basics

Valerie VanBooven RN, BSN, CMC

Medicare is a federal health insurance program for people 65 and older, and certain people with disabilities, or ESRD (End Stage Renal Disease). It pays for much of your health care, but not all of it. There are some costs you will have to pay yourself.

There are other kinds of health insurance that may help pay the costs that Medicare does not.

Medicare Supplements (Medigap Policies) and Long Term Care Insurance will pick up some of the costs that Medicare will not pay for.

What will Medicare pay?

Medicare comes in 2 parts.

Medicare Part A and Part B.

Medicare Part A is Hospital Insurance.

Part A pays for inpatient hospital care, **some** skilled nursing facility care, hospice care, and **some** home health care.

Most people get Medicare Part A automatically when they turn 65. There is no premium or monthly payment for Part A.

Medicare Part B is Medical Insurance.

Part B pays for doctor's services, outpatient hospital care, and some other medical services that Part A doesn't pay for. Part B pays for these services and supplies when they are medically necessary.

Part B has a premium that is currently $50.00 per month. Rates change every year.

What will Medicare A and B NOT pay for?

Medicare carries some high deductibles. For instance, during a hospital stay, you will automatically have a $792 deductible for days 1-60. On day 61, you are responsible for $198 (your deductible) per day through day 90. On day 91, you pay $365 per day (your deductible) through day 150.

For a skilled nursing facility stay, Medicare pays for days 1-20. On day 21 you pay $99.00 per day deductible through day 100.

Medicare will pay for the first 3 pints of blood. Also, you will be responsible for 20% for most covered services under Part B; 50% for outpatient mental health treatment, and a copay for outpatient hospital services.

Medicare was never designed to pay for **long-term care.** In other words, if you will be living in a nursing home, or if you will need around the clock care at home, Medicare does not pay for these services. It was never designed to. Medicare is for acute medical care, and rehabilitative care only.

A Medicare Supplement or Medigap policy will cover some or all of the deductibles described above. This is a policy that you will have to purchase separately. Medicare supplements will **not** pay for long-term care costs. They simply cover the deductibles under Medicare and sometimes pay for a few extras.

Long Term Care Insurance will not cover Medicare deductibles like a Medigap policy will, but LTC Insurance will pay for all of the costs associated with long term nursing home care, in-home care, assisted living, and adult daycare.

For more information on Medicare Part A and B, or for information on choosing a Medicare Supplement, call 1-800-MEDICARE, or look on the web at *www.medicare.gov*

Understanding Medicaid

Valerie VanBooven RN, BSN, CMC

Medicaid was established by federal law (Title XIX of the Social Security Act), and is administered by each state individually. Medicaid is a program for poor or "impoverished" people, and people with high medical costs. Congress established Medicaid to provide a "safety net" for people who had no other way to pay for their health care or long-term care.

Medicaid is the long-term care payer of last resort for the frail elderly, persons with mental retardation, and those with physical or developmental disabilities.

Most long-term care and services such as prescription drugs, eyeglasses, and dental care are provided at each states discretion. When money is scarce, these services may be the most vulnerable, not because of ill will on the part of the state decision makers, but because there may be nowhere else to cut.

Medicaid is a highly flawed program. States continue to make decisions about Medicaid that, among other things, will affect the amount of long-term care assistance available in each state, the eligibility criteria and number of persons eligible for that assistance, and the types of services that will be reimbursed. The way in which the states provide services under Medicaid will shape the delivery system on which more comprehensive long-term care will be built.

"Income Cap" States vs "Medically Needy" States

A state may provide long-term care services in nursing facilities or private community settings to persons whose gross income (without deductions) falls under an "income cap" set by the states.

The income cap is generally set at 3 times the SSI standard (currently $1,635). The eligible person must the income he or she has to pay for the cost of nursing home care, and the state will pay the balance of the cost.

The income cap is absolute. A person whose income is $1 above the cutoff cannot get any assistance from Medicaid even though they have no other way to pay for care. This is commonly known as the "Medicaid Gap", and no spend down of income is allowed.

Income cap states include:

> Alabama
> Alaska
> Arkansas
> Colorado
> Delaware
> Florida
> Idaho
> Louisiana
> Mississippi
> Nevada
> New Mexico
> Oklahoma
> Oregon
> South Carolina
> South Dakota
> Texas
> Wyoming

The rest of the states are described as "medically needy" states.

In a "medically needy" state, a person who has too much income to qualify for Medicaid services, but has high medical or long-term care bills, can "spend down" their assets in order to qualify.

Their SSI income will go directly to the nursing facility to pay bills, and Medicaid will pick up the rest. In most "medically needy" states, an individual can have no more than $999.99-$2000.00 in assets.

Assets that must be spent down in order to qualify include:

* Cash
* Checking/ saving accounts
* C.D.'s
* Savings bonds
* Investment accounts/mutual funds/ stocks
* IRA's and other retirement accounts
* Vacation homes and investment properties
* Second car
* Certain real estate or personal property not in use
* Anything that has value that can be converted to cash

Assets that a person can keep include:

* A home, (a principal residence)
* Household goods
* Personal effects
* Automobile—one per household
* Life insurance (no more than $1500 in cash surrender value)
* Prepaid burial plan and space or designated life insurance policy up to $1500.00
* Property essential to the individual's self support
* Income producing property—other than cash, with some restrictions

Transferring Assets

When a person applies for Medicaid to pay for long-term care, federal law requires the state to consider recent transfers of assets and gifting. If a person or his or her spouse has transferred assets for less then fair market value in the 36 months prior to applying for Medicaid, or at any time after applying, the applicant will be considered "ineligible" for a period of time based on the amount transferred. In the case of assets transferred to a "trust" the look back period is 60 months.

Estate Recovery

With the changes in federal law enacted in August 1993, the state must seek recovery of Medicaid expenditures from the estate of a deceased individual who was 55 or older when he or she received assistance. The state must include all real and personal property and other assets included within an estate under the state's probate law. The state may include other property in which the individual had an interest at the time of death. If the deceased Medicaid recipient has a spouse still living in the home (community spouse), the state will usually not seek recovery until the time of the spouse's death.

Recommendations

Talk to a professional, such as an Elder Law Attorney, Estate Planning Attorney, Financial Advisor, or Geriatric Care Manager prior to applying to Medicaid. Explore all options and resources prior to application.

Sources of Information in Each State

State offices, such as the director of the state agency responsible for Medicaid, the office responsible for administering home and community based services under Medicaid in your state, the office responsible for Alzheimer programs or the Alzheimer's Disease task force (only in some states), division of family services, department of aging, or department of health and human services, are examples of places to start asking for information on Medicaid.

Other advocates that may be excellent resources in your state, include the long-term care ombudsman, legal services (contact your bar association), organizations representing older people (AARP, Older Women's League), and organizations representing persons with other disabilities.

What is Long-term Care Insurance?

Valerie VanBooven RN, BSN, CMC

Long-term Care Insurance is one way to pay for the exorbitant costs of long-term care. On average, the cost of home care and/or nursing home care in the United States today is over $50,000 per year. Most individuals have a difficult time affording that cost. Medicare does not pay for long-term care. Medicaid does pay for long-term care, but the individual must essentially be impoverished in order to qualify.

Forty-six percent of people over age 65 will need some form of long-term care in their lifetimes. Many will begin needing care at home, and then transition to a nursing care facility at some time. The average length of stay in a nursing home is about 2.8 years.

Long-term Care Insurance (LTCi) will pay for most or all of long-term care costs. It was introduced in the 1980's as "nursing home" insurance. Today, the situation is much different. LTCi pays for nursing home care, assisted living, in-home care, and adult daycare.

Long-term Care Insurance (LTCi) should be purchased when the individual is healthy, and has had no major illnesses or hospitalizations. Therefore, if your loved one has already been diagnosed with Alzheimer's Disease, dementia, memory loss, stroke, Parkinson's Disease, Lou Gehrig's Disease (ALS), MS, or any other long-term chronic condition, they will not qualify.

However, as adult children of aging parents, especially if those parents have suffered from one of these potentially hereditary diseases, it is imperative that you investigate LTCi, and talk to an insurance professional about coverage.

When investigating LTCi, look for a company that has an AM Best Rating of A+ or better. Also consider assets of the company, how long they have been in the LTCi business, and how many current policy holders they have.

Choose a policy that will best suit your needs in the future, and will best suit your financial means. If you have assets to protect, want to avoid Medicaid in the future, and would prefer to be cared for at home for as long as possible, LTCi might be an option for you.

One way to obtain objective information about LTCi is to request a copy of "A Shopper's Guide to Long-term Care Insurance". This guide is published by the National Association of Insurance Commissioners, and is available for free through any insurance agent, or on the web at www.naic.org.

Tax qualified plans have some tax advantages at the Federal level, and most states will also offer additional tax advantages on premiums.

If your loved one currently has a Long-term Care Insurance policy, call their agent immediately, or call customer service and get the claims process started right away. The benefits are tremendous. Often our aging adults can stay at home longer, or be placed in the nursing home of their choice, simply because they chose to insure themselves against the risk of needing long-term care.

Geriatric Care Management as a Resource

Valerie VanBooven RN, BSN, CMC

When faced with decisions regarding long-term care for an aging loved one, a geriatric care manager may be one of the best private resources in your area. A geriatric care manager has extensive knowledge of all local resources related to aging and caregiving.

Geriatric care managers can be located nationwide. They assist with coordination of care for aging and disabled adults.

This service is provided in a series of steps including initial assessment, care plan development, implementation of services, and quality of care monitoring. Geriatric care managers are typically nurses, social workers, gerontologists, physical therapists, occupational therapists, or other human service professionals.

The "care management" process can improve the quality of life not only for the aging adult, but also for the caregivers and family members involved. The service is very personalized and utilizes the same principals of "case management".

Most geriatric care managers are available to the family and client 24 hours per day, 7 days per week. The ultimate goal is to keep the aging adult in the home for as long as safely possible. In-home care can be arranged at any level of need to accommodate the client and the family. Geriatric care managers often will be asked to arrange other services for the client such as bill paying, housekeeping, lawn care, transportation to appointments, grocery shopping, meal delivery, and personal care issues.

When the client is in need of transition to alternative living arrangements like nursing home, assisted living, or even independent retirement communities, the care manager often can recommend the best facilities that meet the clients financial needs.

Geriatric Care Management is truly a holistic approach to caring for the aging adult. All resources available are utilized to assist families when long-term care is needed.

Care managers are also often asked to troubleshoot quality concerns with nursing homes and home care agencies. Their level of professionalism and knowledge of the local regulations and laws are of great value to the family. They are considered "advocates" for the elderly.

Geriatric care management is paid for privately by client and family members, Medicare and Medicaid do not cover these services. However, Long-term Care Insurance does cover some or all of the care management fee.

Most geriatric care managers belong to the National Association of Professional Geriatric Care Managers. In order to find a care manager in your area, you can search for one through their website at www.caremanager.org

Geriatric care management services can save the family both time and money, and ultimately decrease the stress and frustration of the caregiver. The process gives the family and the aging adult the opportunity to make informed and appropriate decisions regarding any long-term care needs.

They're Speaking Greek

Anne R. Lindsay, Ph.D.

Serious medical conditions mean entering what is a new world for many people: the world of medical lingo and hospitals. It can feel overwhelming at times. How adept individual physicians are at communicating complicated medical information to lay persons varies greatly. Indeed, medical language is based, in large part, on Greek and Latin. Without translations or good communication skills on the part of treating medical personnel, people often leave medical facilities as confused, or more, than before speaking with doctors, nurses, and other affiliated personnel.

Even with the best communication, people often go numb after hearing feared diagnoses, including Alzheimer's disease. For many people, little is heard or heard accurately at that point so a medical team's ability to recognize this phenomenon and deal with it effectively is important.

Your willingness to ask questions, even days later if needed, is also an important part of the process. If you cannot think of questions at the time of diagnosis, write all of your questions and those of family members down in the following days or weeks and contact your physician with them when you feel ready.

In this section, I hope to provide you with basic information about Alzheimer's disease, diagnostic processes, and the language you may encounter. What you will find here is an overview, not an in-depth description.

The overview may seem technical, but it is important to your understanding of Alzheimer's disease. Again, these are terms many of you will encounter during the course of the illness.

People are often confused when they hear "dementia," which is often taken to mean Alzheimer's disease. In fact, the term dementia covers illnesses that often look and progress quite differently. Alzheimer's disease is a specific kind of dementia with its own characteristics.

I will refer frequently to cognition. Cognition, or cognitive functions, refers to what most people mean when they use terms like thinking or thought. As the doctors and other professionals you will encounter use the term, it encompasses thinking, knowing, awareness, the ability to use judgment, and learning.

Alzheimer's disease is a dementing illness, one of a number of such conditions. Dementia, which I'll also refer to as dementing illnesses, is a blanket term that indicates the individual has an illness that will cause progressive deterioration of most or all cognitive functions. It is further classified by some professionals as a "cortical dementia," as contrasted with "subcortical dementias" that are sometimes associated with, for example, Parkinson's and Huntington's diseases or "mixed dementias," such as multiinfarct dementia (the build up effect of many and continued small strokes). The specific differences between the three types of dementia are beyond the scope of this overview. The distinction between cortical and subcortical dementias can be somewhat misleading as they both usually contain some overlapping symptoms and damage to brain areas, but generally refers to the areas of the brain most affected by the dementing processes. The difference between the two types is mentioned only to clarify that the current overview refers only to cortical dementia, with Alzheimer's disease as the prototype.

We typically think of dementias as conditions that affect only the elderly. While they do occur primarily in the elderly, they can also appear in younger persons due to a variety of medical conditions and sometimes traumatic neurological events. In the case of Alzheimer's disease, we differentiate between early onset Alzheimer's disease and the type of Alzheimer's that is found in the elderly, sometimes referred to as senile dementia of the Alzheimer's type (SDAT). While there appear to be different causes of the two types of Alzheimer's, the appearance and progression of the disease is superficially essentially the same in younger and older persons. Aside from the age at onset of the disease, one of the major differences between the two types appears to be genetic, with a higher incidence of genetic transmission in the early onset type.

There is support for the notion that the overall degree of dementia is the same within the two groups, but different cognitive functions tend to be affected at different times. Specifically, early-onset may affect relatively more language functions (left brain) early in the course of the disease whereas late-onset may affect relatively more visuo-spatial functions (right brain) early on (Kensinger, 1996).

Cortical dementias of all kinds have in common a deterioration of global cognitive functioning. This is opposed to, for example, a stroke where one area of the brain is damaged in a single, sudden event. Whereas with a stroke or other event which primarily impact circumscribed areas of the brain are likely to cause cognitive problems associated with that area of the brain, dementing conditions affect the whole brain, and thus all cognitive functions. Which functions will be most affected and when they are affected depends on the particular illness and, to some degree, individual differences. In Alzheimer's disease, memory impairments and personality changes tend to he the first noticeable symptoms.

There are misconceptions about cognition and aging. Although there are some slight changes in limited areas of memory and other cognitive functions as we age, these are not changes that affect daily functioning to any significant degree. In fact, there are far fewer changes than people often expect. By contrast, the changes that begin to occur in early Alzheimer's disease affect daily living— job skills deteriorate, initiating even routine behaviors such as bathing may falter, moods may be labile (swing from one mood to another), other personality changes may occur, ability to function as efficiently as in the past during daily life begins to show impairments, people often become disoriented and get lost in familiar surroundings, and so on. These are not the common memory failures and other slips we all experience; these are repeated symptoms of a serious problem and are impacting the individual's ability to function independently.

The transitional zone between the normal cognitive changes that come with aging and the onset of Alzheimer's disease is sometimes called a period of "mild cognitive impairment (MCI)." Developing mild cognitive impairment as we age is a strong predictor of later developing Alzheimer's disease. However, with MCI a person retains all cognitive skills except for short-term memory skills. While reasoning and abstract thinking abilities remain normal for the individual, short-term memory is distinctly impaired. And not everyone who develops MCI will go on to develop Alzheimer's disease. Your chances of developing Alzheimer's within four years after being diagnosed with MCI are 50-50. The putative cause of both is a deterioration of the hippocampus, an area of the brain critical for short-term memory. While this area of the brain shrinks some with normal aging, the shrinkage is more pronounced with MCI and, in Alzheimer's, the shrinkage is more rapid and more pronounced. Some researchers and physicians are now advocating the benefits of using drugs currently in use for early to moderate Alzheimer's early on when a person is diagnosed with MCI.

Our brains are remarkable machines, if you will. We rarely consider the intricate series of events that occur to make we humans function as smoothly as we do. The series of events go, for example, from single cells in our sensory systems detecting exterior stimuli such as light to setting off a chain of electrical and chemical events involving potentially thousands of brain cells (neurons) to move that information to areas of our brains that can detect the light, and then send it to different areas of the brain that interpret the light as coming from a bulb in an intricate chandelier. Further integration is necessary to realize that the structure is a "chandelier," which requires memory for the name and the structure as one we recognize as a lighting fixture with that particular name. We may even have an emotional reaction to the fixture such as, "it's beautiful—it reminds me of the one I saw at the Plaza." While this may seem simple, it requires activation and integration of different areas of the brain, all of which must be in working order for the final emotional reaction to occur.

We rely on that global functioning of the brain, the integration of the millions of cells and all of the chemicals in the brain to function. In humans, that intricate remarkable organ has evolved to the point where we can initiate our thoughts, puzzle them through, work through problems, generate solutions to the problems, and act on the solutions. Global cognitive functions include a wide spectrum of abilities: attention and concentration; impulse control; intelligence; complex thought; learning and memory; reasoning, and organization of information; expressive functions (e.g., verbal communication), receptive functions (e.g., understanding speech; integrating incoming sensory information), and so on. We also rely on intact brain functioning for a relatively stable psychological status. In a healthy brain, imbalances of specific chemicals and sometimes abnormal functioning of certain areas of the brain can cause depression, schizophrenia, obsessive compulsive disorder, and a whole host of other psychiatric illnesses. Imagine how vulnerable the person with Alzheimer's disease is to experiencing many of the same symptoms of these disorders when his or her brain is so fragile and vulnerable. Some of the functions are more basic, ones that we take for granted such as dressing ourselves—they're learned during childhood and become relatively automatic. These often are, in fact, skilled acts that require motor programming, something that is eventually lost in Alzheimer's disease.

Dementing conditions also have an insidious onset—sometimes it is so slow and subtle that early symptoms are frequently missed by family, the affected individual, and physicians. There are times when a previously undetected dementia will suddenly become more evident with symptoms more pronounced. Fevers, infections, head trauma, and surgery are all examples of events that may cause subtle symptoms to become more conspicuous and possibly accelerate the cognitive impairments. Psychosocial stress may also sometimes cause early symptoms to become more exaggerated.

In other sections of this book you will find information about early symptoms of Alzheimer's disease, as well as the later stages. For the vast majority of people, memory failures and personality changes are the first noticeable symptoms. Mild verbal problems, such as word finding difficulties, may also be noted very early in the disease. It is important to note, though, that for a relative minority of people there may be variations in the early symptoms, with memory problems appearing somewhat later than other early symptoms. Significant changes in cognition or personality warrant a physician's attention as either may be signs that there is a medical problem.

There are reversible conditions that may mimic early Alzheimer's disease. Most notable of these is depression. In the elderly, depression may take on the appearance of a pseudodementia—a condition which is not a true dementia but which is, instead, a psychiatric condition that appears very like the early stages of Alzheimer's disease and other dementing conditions. Differentiating among the possible causes of cognitive and behavioral changes requires a professional evaluation. What one may expect when visiting a physician with concerns about possible dementia, and how to prepare for the visit, will be discussed later in this section.

Other treatable conditions and variables that can mimic Alzheimer's disease include Vitamin B12 deficiency, medication side effects and medication interactions, nutritional deficiencies, and other metabolic or hormonal abnormalities.

Alzheimer's disease is known by some professionals as the disease with "the four A's." These are hallmark symptoms associated with the disease and include agnosia, apraxia, amnesia, and aphasia. I will only delve into the most basic definition of each condition in this context, but it is important to know why your loved one behaves the way he or she does and, to do so, one needs to understand the basic neuropsychological processes of Alzheimer's disease. These are also terms you may hear over and over during the course of your loved one's illness, and so a rudimentary familiarity with them will help you to understand more easily the language attached to your loved one's medical conditions.

Agnosia is loss of the ability to recognize or know what it is we perceive. Sensory organs are intact but the individual loses the ability to attach meaning to the incoming sensory information. Thus, what the intact healthy brain perceives as a "mitten" may become a meaningless object in the environment of someone with Alzheimer's disease.

Apraxia is the inability to carry out a skilled act. Even behaviors that we consider simple are often planned series of skilled acts. Think about teaching a toddler how to dress—what we later take for granted takes a toddler some time and effort to learn. These behaviors, though, are eventually programmed into skilled acts we undertake automatically. Even something as simple as knowing how to wave goodbye or blow out a match is a skilled program. These programs are slowly lost during the course of Alzheimer's disease. I have often listened to families frustrated with a parent who has Alzheimer's disease and who "refuses" to dress. It is important to understand that, in addition to other cognitive disruptions, he or she likely does not remember the sequence and that it is a skilled behavior that he or she is eventually no longer capable of undertaking independently.

Amnesia is the symptom most people think of regarding Alzheimer's disease. It is a blanket term that refers to memory loss. We often think of memory as a unitary entity—it is not. Memory is complex and the types of memories lost may be varied, as exhibited in most cases of "amnesia" and throughout the course of Alzheimer's disease. There are different kinds of memory. Immediate or sensory memory is a type of memory that decays rapidly if not moved into short-term memory. It is memory for incoming sensory information. Seeing a phone number written down, for example, is a sensory register that if not actively stored (by another kind of memory, working memory) in short-term memory, will rapidly decay. Storage in short-term memory generally takes some processing work (working memory) to move the information from immediate memory to short-term memory. Short-term memory has a limited span and can hold only fairly small amounts of information before it is either committed to long-term memory or is forgotten. Moving information into long-term memory is best achieved through active processing such as rehearsal of the information, repetition, and manipulating the information in a way that gives it meaning to the person trying to store it in memory. Long-term memory appears to have a relatively limitless capacity and, barring brain damage, is permanent. Remote memory refers to memory for past events. Although even some degree of remote memory appears to be lost early in Alzheimer's disease (Green & Hodges, 1996a; Green & Hodges, 1996b; Beatty & Salmon, 1991; Beatty & Bernstein, 1989), it is working memory and short-term memory that are most glaringly impaired during early Alzheimer's disease. Forgetting that one has eaten breakfast and claiming that family members are "trying to starve me," is an example of working, short-term, and ultimately long-term memory failure. We know from years of neuropsychological evaluations of persons with Alzheimer's disease that the individual has not maintained the information long enough in short-term memory and has not been able to process it to store in long-term memory the fact that he or she ate breakfast.

Finally, aphasia refers to the loss of language ability. Aphasia can be expressive (ability to speak comprehensibly) or receptive (ability to understand language). Early in Alzheimer's disease, the ability to speak is usually mildly affected. Words or names that are used infrequently are generally the first affected—that is, they are the first kinds of words that the individual has difficulty recalling. With disease progression, more commonly used words and names will be difficult to recall and thus use. Grammar, too, will be affected so that after a while, the individual's speech may make little sense. Speech comprehension is also increasingly impaired. Readers will note that in the section on communication elsewhere in this book it is recommended that communications to the person with Alzheimer's disease be kept short and simple. This is because sentences that are long and/or syntactically complex are difficult and sometimes impossible for the person with Alzheimer's disease to process and understand.

There are other cognitive functions that become impaired. Perhaps most important among these are impairments in initiation, impulse control, insight, judgment, ability to think abstractly, and reasoning. All of these combine with the memory problems to lead to dangerous situations if proper supervision is not provided as Alzheimer's progresses.

Note that all of these symptoms may wax and wane. Your loved one may seem completely normal one day and exhibit significant impairments the next. Even later in the course of the disease, symptoms may fluctuate. Alzheimer's is persistent and progressive, so some fluctuations may actually mean that there is a different process in place, such as depression. But particularly early in the course if Alzheimer's, some variation in ability is expected. Family members often cling to the good days or hours as signs that the diagnosis is wrong, as Deborah's mother did. Be prepared for good days and bad days, good hours and bad hours, as they are part of the normal course of the disease.

This most likely happens for two reasons: first, the brain is not uniformly affected. While some areas of the brain are impacted early in the disease, others are spared until later in the disease. So some functions remain relatively intact while others begin to deteriorate quite early. Second, our brains have many connections. These connections of cells in the brain are responsible for sending messages all around the brain and, ultimately, to the body (as well as receiving information from the body). During the "good" times, the instances when the individual can perform a task he previously couldn't for example, the connections are working. Either the connection is only partially damaged and messages get through sporadically, or the brain has been able to find a different route to send the message. As time progresses, connections are more completely severed and cells that previously provided routes around the damaged area are also damaged and die.

Personality changes are also a hallmark of Alzheimer's disease. Often early in the course of the disease, people may seem apathetic, increasingly withdraw from socializing, and exhibit mood swings (emotional lability). The individual with the disease may become easily irritable or agitated, and occasionally even aggressive. Socially inappropriate behavior may be increasingly prominent and embarrassing for families. Remember at these times that it is the disease asserting itself and save your embarrassment for other occasions where we really do something silly to embarrass ourselves! The changes in personality and psychiatric status are not the fault of your loved one, they are the fault of a noxious disease process. There are suggestions for addressing these behaviors and problems found elsewhere in this book.

Why do all of these cognitive and behavioral changes occur? Without delving into a neuroscience lesson, it is because of the changes in the structure and functioning of the brain. A certain degree of brain atrophy (shrinkage) is normal as we age. In the Alzheimer's brain, atrophy is accelerated and far more severe than normally seen. Neurons (brain cells) that normally keep us thinking and behaving according to our norms are being lost. Those that remain work increasingly poorly.

Dr. Delacourte refers to neurofibrillary "tangles" and "plaques." The "plaques" he is referring to are the amyloid plaques that are one of the biological hallmarks of the disease. These plaques are made up of proteins that, in healthy individuals, would be eliminated as the brain eliminates other waste products. In the Alzheimer's brain, these beta-amyloid waste products accumulate to form hard plaques between brain cells, thus interrupting or stopping normal brain functioning. We depend on chemical and electrical transmission between brain cells for our thought processes, and the plaques that form in the brains of people with Alzheimer's interferes with the transmission.

Neurofibrillary tangles are also found in other dementing conditions but tend to be numerous in the brain of someone with Alzheimer's disease, increasing as the disease progresses. These tangles form inside brain cells in people with Alzheimer's disease and they ultimately interfere with the ability of cells to take in nutrients, eventually leading to cell death.

What causes Alzheimer's disease and the specific brain pathology is fodder for books. In short, we do not really know what causes Alzheimer's disease. In SDAT, there appears to be some genetic component but in the type of Alzheimer's disease that strikes people over age sixty-five, the genetic component is relatively small. Environmental causes have been hypothesized to contribute, such as aluminum building up in the brain, but there has yet to be an environmental cause (or causes) that has been satisfactorily proved to contribute.

In their search to better understand the disease and find a cure, researchers such as Dr. Delacourte and Dr. Gautier are actively trying to understand the causes of Alzheimer's disease. Among the many changes that occur in the brain of a person with Alzheimer's disease, a neurochemical (important chemicals that function in the brain) called acetylcholine is depleted, particularly in the temporal lobe, an area important for memory. I mention this one change in brain functioning because it is a current target of Alzheimer's treatment. Specifically, there are drugs now in use that have been shown to help improve memory and sometimes behavior during the early and middle stages of Alzheimer's disease. There is no guarantee that they will work in every person or will work to the degree that families hope, but they are an improvement. These drugs are known as cholinesterase inhibitors.

Acetylcholinesterase is the enzyme that breaks down the neurochemical acetylcholine in the brain. Acetylcholine, along with other neurochemicals, is important for many brain functions, including memory and other cognitive processes. By inhibiting the production of that enzyme, more acetylcholine is available for use in the brain, thus enhancing brain function. There are currently four such drugs that are FDA approved for use in Alzheimer's disease: (generic names are listed first followed by brand names in parentheses) donepezil (Aricept), tacrine (Cognex), galantamine (Reminyl), rivastigmine (Exelon), and memantine (Namenda). Memantine (Namenda) is the only one of these drugs that is approved for use in moderate to late Alzheimer's disease—the other drugs are effective only in the early to early-middle stages. If your physician does not suggest taking any of these medications, ask about them. Which medication is appropriate for you depends on numerous factors that you will need to discuss with your doctor.

They will not be appropriate for all people and do not tend to help in late stage Alzheimer's.

Many people turn to "natural" remedies when they are faced with a serious illness. While these can sometimes be efficacious, they can also be harmful if not taken correctly or by someone who should not take them. In the case of Alzheimer's disease, for example, some research has supported the use of ginkgo biloba to slightly improve memory for some individuals. This is not, however, a benign "natural supplement"—one of its side effects is the possibility of decreasing the ability of the blood to clot. Because there are many such side effects, interactions with other medications and foods, little knowledge about dosages, and other variables it is *imperative* that you check with your physician before taking any natural supplements.

Since I have taken some time here to discuss treatment with medications, let me take a moment to suggest that you consult with your physician(s) regarding medications for other symptoms as they arise. Hallucinations, for example, may be part of they symptom picture as time progresses, or sometimes early in the disease as they were with Deborah's father. There are medications available to treat these and other symptoms. Particularly in the elderly, medication side effects can be serious and you will need to weigh with your treating physician the potential risks and benefits of various medication options. Again, do not be afraid to ask questions and make suggestions. You can help by doing as the women in this book have suggested and keep notes, a symptom journal if you will. To use the same example, it is important to know if your loved one hallucinates only in the evening, in which case he or she is probably "sundowning" (becoming symptomatic around the time of day that the sun sets), a common phenomenon in dementing conditions. Diurnal variation (changes symptoms at different times of day) occurs for all of us (e.g., feeling sleepy at about 3:00 p.m., as so many of us do). It can be more problematic for someone with Alzheimer's disease, and knowing that hallucinations are part of sundowning versus a pattern that does not follow any diurnal pattern is important for treatment considerations.

I hope I have succeeded in translating some of the language you will hear as you traverse the medical language you will encounter. There is a glossary included at the end of this book for those terms you encounter (and there may be many) that I have not explained, and there are also web addresses for sites that can provide more information. I want to take some time not to talk about seeking a diagnosis and the diagnostic process.

Something almost universal happens when we visit physicians with concerns about symptoms—we forget half of what we meant to communicate about symptoms and concerns. It can be an intimidating process visiting a physician, particularly when you suspect something may be seriously wrong with someone you love. We often feel rushed in busy doctors' offices, there may be interpersonal variables between the physician and you that makes communication difficult, and when you factor in the emotional stress of the situation, forgetting is almost inevitable. It is therefore important to prepare yourself for the visit.

Write down everything that you want to communicate to the doctor. If you use a computer, make a list on your computer that you can give to the doctor. Make it brief (preferably one page, no more than two pages) and highlight important information. Include general concerns, specific events that you think are good examples of the problems your loved one has been having (e.g., getting lost in his or her own neighborhood), and a chronological history of your loved one's symptoms put together as best you can remember. Your physician will also want to know about family medical and psychiatric history. If you are not aware of your family's medical history, do your best to find out before visiting the doctor. You do not need to list each little bump and bruise in your family's medical history, but do list the important medical information for your loved one, his or her family of origin, and any significant medical conditions that appear often in your family. Be sure to include any accidents your loved one might have had, particularly those that may have caused head injury, or which caused documented head injury. This is because head injury is a risk factor for Alzheimer's disease and other dementing conditions. In the elderly, a mild head injury can also cause confusion and other problems that are related only to the head injury. Even a mild infection or dehydration can cause confusion in the elderly, sometimes reaching a state of delirium, so attention to your loved one's habits is also important. Most of these are variables that can be ruled out by physician testing, but the more information you can provide the better. Also list all medications, dosages, and when they are taken. Some physicians prefer you to bring the medications with you. The elderly are often on multiple medications and their combination can sometimes cause confusion, other cognitive problems, and psychiatric side-effects so it is important not to leave out any information about medication. Your list should include prescription medications, over-the-counter medications, and any natural supplements your loved one takes. If there is a history of substance abuse, be honest about it—a sustained history of alcohol and other substance abuse can cause cognitive dysfunctions very similar to those found in Alzheimer's disease.

There are other important variables I always ask about. A neuropsychologist sometimes asks different questions than physicians, but all are pertinent and may be relevant in your loved one's case. Work history, for example, is important if he or she worked around toxic chemicals—some of these can cause brain damage and thus cognitive decline. If your loved one has worked in an environment where you think chemicals might be an issue, be sure to include that in your summary for the physician. Educational level is also important, as is area of specialization in education and career. While you will want to note general alterations in cognition and behavior, anything specific that is a notable change in your loved one is important. I know, for instance, that there is a serious problem when I encounter an architect who cannot replicate a simple block figure. Similarly, anyone (from any educational background) who could previously do complicated math in his or her head and now cannot add simple numbers on paper is notable for a significant change in functioning versus individuals who always had difficulty with even simple math. If your family member has preexisting learning problems, is illiterate, or his/her last grade completed in school was second grade, indicate that for your physician. You do not want someone interpreting an inability to read a simple command on a test as a sign of a new cognitive problem when, in fact, he or she never would have been able to do so. If he or she had special cognitive abilities or talents that have changed, again, indicate that change and the nature of the change.

One often does not know what to expect when visiting a physician, particularly when there are concerns about serious medical conditions and diagnosis. If you have followed my advice, you will arrive at the physician's office prepared with notes to jog your memory and, preferably, a short history you can hand to the doctor. The type of physician you will see often depends on your location. Your loved one's primary physician may make the diagnosis or refer to a specialist, usually a neurologist or a gerontologist. Often, particularly when people live in remote areas where medical care is sparse, specialists are not available and a primary care physician will make the diagnosis.

The evaluation with the physician can be uncomfortable, as Deborah noted when she and her family visited the doctor with concerns about his behavior. It requires talking about issues that make us uncomfortable and may upset the family member who is having difficulties. As lovely as it would be to avoid talking about these issues, it is essential that your concerns be discussed openly with the doctor. A large portion of an evaluation for dementia is the clinical exam and history. One recent piece of research estimates that between seventy-five percent and ninety percent of cases of dementia are missed in primary care settings, including sometimes severe dementia (Gifford & Cummings, 1999). Without access to your observations and concerns, the physician may miss a diagnosis. Importantly, he or she may also miss diagnosis of a treatable and reversible condition.

Alzheimer's is a diagnosis made by exclusion. That means that in order to make the diagnosis, the physician must rule out all other causes consistent with the symptom picture. Sometimes the symptoms are glaring by the time the diagnosis is made, other times they are not as obvious and it may take a while and many evaluations to make a diagnosis.

Because settings may be so different, the physician from whom you seek help may diverge slightly from the below. The clinical interview is an important part of the diagnosis. Pertinent family members should be involved as the patient may forget or try to minimize any problems he or she has been having. The diagnostic process should include at least a brief mental status examination to assess attention, memory, expressive and receptive language, executive functions (abstract reasoning, judgment, calculation, etc.), visuospatial skills, and praxis (to look for apraxias). There are standard mental status examinations such as the Mini-Mental State Examination (MMSE; Folstein, Folstein, & McHugh, 1975) that should take about fifteen minutes to administer. Scores on these standardized evaluations can then be compared to normative values for your loved one's age group, which is particularly important if there are only mild impairments and/or the physician is not expert at administering mental status exams. Changes in psychological status and personality should be assessed via observation of the patient during the evaluation and by interviewing family members.

Although there are current laboratory tests that can sometimes identify certain indicators consistent with Alzheimer's disease, these are not yet regularly used for a variety of reasons. Most important to know is that there is currently no blood test that is a definitive diagnostic measure for Alzheimer's disease. Blood and urine tests should be taken, though, to rule out other treatable conditions, such as vitamin B12 deficiency.

Although I frequently hear about people who are diagnosed without the use of structural imaging, such as MRI or CT scans, I believe this is a mistake and scans should be performed if at all possible. I hear this most from people who live in rural areas and do not have ready access to more sophisticated medical technology. If your physician recommends one travel day for the purposes of getting a brain scan, it is worth the effort. Both CT and MRI scans take fairly detailed images of the brain (sort of like x-rays of bones) and can provide a significant amount of information, including data that can help to make the diagnosis. For example, on an image of a brain of a person with early Alzheimer's disease one might see atrophy in the medial temporal lobe of the brain. This is an area of the brain important for memory and one that tends to show the effects of Alzheimer's disease on brain scans earlier than other brain areas.

A small degree of overall brain atrophy is normal as we age, so mild atrophy in itself is not diagnostic. General brain atrophy beyond that which is expected for the patient's same-age peers is significant though. The brain scan of a person with another kind of dementia, such as that caused by a series of small strokes (multiinfarct dementia), generally looks different from that of someone with Alzheimer's disease so the test can assist in diagnosis. I say generally because there are occasions when even brain scans are inconclusive and sometimes people show signs of small strokes or other problems in addition to signs of Alzheimer's disease. If your physician disagrees with my point of view, know that the clinical criteria (lists of symptoms and the history of the symptoms, the physical examination, and traditional laboratory tests such as blood tests) are currently thorough and should be sufficient for a diagnosis if brain scans are not available to you.

Your loved one's physician may choose to run further tests, particularly if there is a question about diagnosis after all of the more standard tests have been run or the physician wants to rule out other causes for current problems. These may include a SPECT or PET scan, which are functional brain scans (similar to a CT or MRI but measuring blood flow in the brain, which indicates brain functioning in all of the different areas of the brain), a chest x-ray, an electroencephalograph (measures electrical activity in the brain), a lumbar puncture (spinal tap), a toxicology screen, and neuropsychological testing.

A neuropsychologist is a clinical psychologist who specializes in diagnosing and sometimes treating neurologically based problems. If there is a question about diagnosis or treatment, a neuropsychologist may perform a more thorough cognitive and psychological evaluation than the MMSE or other brief screening tests that your physician uses.

Finally, I want to use this section to talk about preparing for the future. There are important issues to think about as we age, and many of us ignore them until it is too late—it is uncomfortable to think about ourselves or someone we love nearing the end of life and having to make decisions associated with this issue in our modern society. Yet some of these will be critical as Alzheimer's disease progresses.

If your loved one does not have a will, it should be completed immediately before he or she cannot express his or her wishes. A living will is also a necessity. Living wills specify what individuals want in terms of life support systems when medical technology is necessary to support life. I cannot tell you how often I have seen families agonize, and too frequently argue, over what a critically ill family member would want in terms of life support. Living wills should not only be in place, but should be detailed and specific. "No heroic measures," for example, is not specific enough. Work with an attorney who has experience in drawing up living wills and who can guide you through the process. You will have to decide what you and/or your family member want to put in your living will. Much of its composition depends on your view of quality of life and variables such as your spiritual beliefs. If you are not sure what to include and exclude in your living will, speak with your physician, an attorney practiced in drawing them up, family, and others who you think can help you make decisions regarding this important document. Some common elements of living wills include "do not resuscitate (DNR)" orders, which instruct medical personnel not to try to revive you through extreme measures such as CPR if your medical condition deteriorates. They should also include whether or not a ventilator (machine used to breathe for an individual who cannot breathe independently) may be used, whether or not a feeding tube is to be used, and what life-extending measures are acceptable or unacceptable. Note that all living wills should include the proviso that the instructions are only valid in the case of irreversible terminal conditions. Again, you should have an attorney practiced in the construction of living wills help you design yours if for no other reason than different states have different regulations regarding these documents.

People with Alzheimer's disease will need someone who can speak for them. This means appointing a trusted individual to make legal decisions for the family member with Alzheimer's disease when he or she is no longer capable of doing so. Similarly, a health care power of attorney (who may be the same person as the individual holding the power of attorney) should be appointed to make medical decisions for the individual with Alzheimer's disease. Finally, a living trust will allow an appointed trustee to manage financial assets when the person with Alzheimer's disease is no longer able to do so independently.

References

Beatty, W.W. & Bernstein, N. (1989). Geographical knowledge in patients with Alzheimer's disease. *Journal of Geriatric Psychiatry and Neurology, 2(2)*, 76-82.

Beatty, W.W. & Salmon, D.P. (1991). Remote memory for visuospatial information in patients with Alzheimer's disease. *Journal of Geriatric Psychiatry and Neurology, 4(1)*, 14-17.

Green, J.D. & Hodges, J.R. (1996). Identification of famous faces and famous names in early Alzheimer's disease. Relationship to anterograde episodic and general semantic memory. *Brain, 119,*111-129.

Green, J.D. & Hodges, J.R. (1996). The fractionation of remote memory. Evidence from a longitudinal study of dementia of Alzheimer type. *Brain, 119*, 129-142.

Kensinger, E. (1996). Early and late onset as subdivisions of Alzheimer's disease. *The Harvard Brain*, 26-29.

Alzheimer's: Causes and Prevention

We do not really know what causes Alzheimer's disease. Based on research, for the majority of people Alzheimer's is likely caused by a variety of factors including age, environment, fitness, personal habits during one's lifetime, and genetics.

The greatest risk factor for all people is increasing age. According to the National Institute on Aging, the incidence of Alzheimer's in America doubles every five years past the age of sixty-five. The Alzheimer's Association reports that about ten percent of Americans aged sixty-five or older have Alzheimer's disease. By age eighty-five, the incidence of Alzheimer's has risen substantially: approximately twenty to fifty percent of persons eight-five or older will develop Alzheimer's disease.

In the general population, the lifetime risk of developing Alzheimer's disease by age sixty-five is about one percent. Risk for people with one parent who has or had Alzheimer's disease rises to ten percent. As we all age, risk for developing the disease increases but, again, the degree of risk for people with one parent who had sporadic late-onset Alzheimer's disease remains only slightly higher than it does for the general population. As the number of people in your family who develop Alzheimer's disease rises, your risk rises, particularly if you have siblings with the disease.

There is much we still do not know about the genetics of Alzheimer's disease, but we have learned about some variables in recent years.

Most professionals currently distinguish between sporadic and familial Alzheimer's disease. Further distinction is made between early and late onset versions of the disease. In general, Alzheimer's that occurs later in life (after age sixty or sixty-five, depending on whose criteria one uses) tends to be sporadic. That is, there is only one case of the disease in a family. Having said that, recall that as we age our risk of developing Alzheimer's increases. So even if you have more than one case of Alzheimer's in your family, if you come from a family where people have lived into their nineties the increased number of family members with Alzheimer's may not mean that you have a more strongly genetic Alzheimer's link, it may simply be an artifact of coming from a family where a number of people have lived long enough to develop the disease in their eighties or nineties, which statistics show us is almost a 50/50 proposition. If these are your parents, you have also grown up in the same environment where they lived, so environmental contributions cannot be eliminated until we know more about the disease and its genetics.

There appears to be a genetic factor in some cases of late-onset, sporadic Alzheimer's disease. Researchers have found that certain forms of the apolipoprotein E (apoE) gene on chromosome 19 can confer greater risk of developing Alzheimer's disease. We all carry apoE, which produces a protein that circulates through our bloodstreams and helps carry cholesterol in the blood. Researchers have found that having one or two copies (that is, inheriting from one parent or two) of the E4 form of apoE can increase risk of developing Alzheimer's. It is far from a perfect understanding about how this works though—you can have two copies of the E4 and never develop Alzheimer's and, conversely, you can develop Alzheimer's without this genetic characteristic present. In fact, half of people who develop Alzheimer's do not have this genetic trait. Other genes are also being investigated and a study recently indicated that there may be another genetic mutation on chromosome 10 that may be linked to Alzheimer's disease (Myers, et al., 2000).

Early onset Alzheimer's is rare, occurring in only five to ten percent of Alzheimer's cases. It can occur as early as 30-years-old. Early onset Alzheimer's has a far stronger genetic link. In familial Alzheimer's researchers have found genetic mutations on chromosomes 1, 14, and 21. Familial Alzheimer's is not a single gene disorder. In single gene disorders, if you carry the gene you will develop the disorder. Familial Alzheimer's has a different kind of inheritance pattern—it is transmitted by autosomal dominance. It is not necessary to go into the specifics or details of autosomal dominance, simply to know that this pattern means that people who inherit the specific genetic mutations have a 50/50 chance of developing the disease. Again, this is a very rare type of Alzheimer's found in only about ten percent of people with Alzheimer's disease, and it tends to be the early onset variety.

Below are other risk factors for the development of Alzheimer's disease:

1   Down's syndrome. After age forty, all people with Down's syndrome develop the brain characteristics seen in Alzheimer's disease, although they do not necessarily develop it to the same degree or develop the kind of dementia seen in Alzheimer's. This link between Down's syndrome and Alzheimer's lead to the discovery of abnormalities on chromosome 21, which is also the chromosome tied to Down's syndrome.

2   Traumatic brain injury. A history of head injury severe enough to cause even fleeting loss of consciousness increases Alzheimer's risk, although the increase in risk level is quite small.

3   Gender. Some research indicates that women are at slightly higher risk of developing Alzheimer's, although this appears mostly in the oldest of Alzheimer's patients. This may, then, be an artifact of longevity with American women generally outliving males. Among people over age ninety, risk tends to be roughly even between men and women.

4   Vascular disease, heart disease, and hypertension (high blood pressure). The association is likely due to vascular problems in the brain.

5   Diabetes mellitus (DM). Two studies (Ott, et al., 1996; Leibson, et al., 1997) have shown a link between DM and

Alzheimer's, again probably due to the vascular problems it can cause in the body, including in the brain, and the associated neuronal (cell) damage that occurs in the brain when there are vascular problems.

6   Aluminum. This variable is controversial. Exposure to high concentrations of aluminum can cause cognitive impairment, as can exposure to many metals and chemicals. Aluminum is found in many different parts of our environments, including food, drinking water, and some medications (e.g., antacids). Rumors about dangers associated with aluminum cooking utensils and the like have been blown out of proportion based on some early research and they have not been substantiated—research to date does not support a link between this kind of everyday, normal level of exposure and Alzheimer's. There has, though, been some research that indicates higher than normal levels of aluminum in drinking water may confer a slightly increased risk (e.g., McLachlan, et al., 1996).

7   Ethnicity. Some research indicates that there are differential rates of Alzheimer's among different ethnic races in the United States. Currently, the rate of Alzheimer's among African Americans and Hispanics is higher than for Caucasian Americans.

Current science and attempts to control genetic inheritance aside, genetic traits are for the most part out of your control. There are, however, preventative steps that you can take now.

The first of these is something that will benefit you no matter what the future holds for you. Researchers at Rush-Presbyterian St. Luke's Medical Center have found that study participants who participate more frequently in cognitively stimulating activity had a lower risk of developing Alzheimer's disease. There are a number of hypotheses underlying the reasons for this finding, but it boils down to the old "use it or lose it" adage. So stay intellectually stimulated—reading, crossword puzzles, logic puzzles, anagrams, museum-going—anything in which you actively engage your mind will help to improve your cognitive status as you age and, according to recent research, may help to prevent Alzheimer's disease.

In the same vein, staying physically healthy is important and may help to prevent a host of diseases, including Alzheimer's disease. There is a close association between stroke and Alzheimer's disease and many people who have Alzheimer's disease have also had small strokes. In addition, new research has found that, particularly in people with certain genetic risk factors, cholesterol (Evans, Emsley, Gao, Sahota, Hall, Farlow, & Hendrie, 2000; Kivipelto, Helkala, Laakso, Hanninen, Hallikainen, Alhainen, Soininen, Tuomilehto, & Nissinen, 2001) and blood pressure levels (Kivipelto, et al., 2001) are risk factors for later development of Alzheimer's disease, with high total cholesterol and high blood pressure separately adding to the risk of developing dementia, and with the two variables combined increasing the risk level even further (Kivipelto, et al.). The research leading to a belief that there are variables within our control that act as protective and risk factors continues to mount—high cholesterol, lack of exercise, obesity, heart disease, and hypertension are all now considered to be possible risk factors for the development of Alzheimer's disease.

You can see that, particularly for those persons who may have a slightly higher risk of developing Alzheimer's due to genetic variables, maintaining a healthy lifestyle and staying cognitively active may be preventative. There are no guarantees—there never are in health or most aspects of life—but the research supports doing what you can to maintain overall physical and cognitive health. For those who are caring for someone with Alzheimer's disease, moderate exercise has also been shown to improve psychological status and overall heath more than caregivers who do not engage in moderate exercise (King, Baumann, O'Sullivan, Wilcox, & Castro, 2002).

Other research suggests that there are issues that you should discuss with your doctor regarding preventative measures. One well-publicized issue is the use of estrogen replacement therapy for women of menopause age. Although estrogen has not been shown to be an effective treatment for women who have already developed Alzheimer's disease (Miller, Monjan, & Buckholtz, 2001), though there is some evidence that adding estrogen replacement therapy enhances the efficacy of tacrine and possibly other cholinesterase drugs (Schneider, Farlow, Henderson, & Pogoda, 1996). However, recent highly publicized and well-conducted research indicates that there are significant risk factors involved with the long-term use of hormone replacement therapy (HRT) and this is an issue you should not only discuss with your doctor but also research carefully before deciding to use HRT.

More promising is research looking at dietary supplements and other variables. Below are issues we recommend you discuss with your physician. Remember, "natural" supplements can be dangerous if misused or when they interact with other medications you may take. You are strongly encouraged to speak with your physician before taking any natural supplement, discuss which supplements might be appropriate for you, and appropriate dosages if you and your physician decide that a supplement may benefit you.

Possible Alzheimer's protective factors include:

1   Antioxidants. One of the damaging aspects of Alzheimer's and other diseases are the free radicals that are released during normal cellular events but which can be harmful. These free radicals can cause what is known as oxidative damage or stress. Some research has supported the use of antioxidants, including vitamins C and E, to counteract the effects of free radicals (Engelhart, et al., 2002).

2   Folic acid and vitamins B6 and B12. Again, before taking any supplement check with your physician. These may confer some protective factor by reducing elevated levels of the amino acid homocysteine in the blood.

3   Education. Some research supports the finding that higher levels of education provide protection. It may be that this is a reflection of the brain's tendency to sprout more and

stronger connections with learning. The well known "Nun Study" showed that even those women who had developed Alzheimer's derived protective factors from intellectual stimulation. Regardless of past education level, there is strong evidence that staying intellectually active confers some degree of protection.

4 Alipoprotein (apoE) E2 may be protective.

5 Anti-inflammatory drugs. Nonsteroidal anti-inflammatory drugs (NSAIDs, such as Advil and Aleve) have been shown in some studies to confer some degree of protection possibly by counteracting the inflammatory events shown present in the brain of people with Alzheimer's disease. NSAIDs come in both over-the-counter and prescription form. Again, these are *drugs* and, particularly if one is considering taking them on a regular basis, must be discussed with a physician before using them on a regular basis. They have side effects and your personal health history may make it dangerous to use them regularly.

6 Statin drugs. Statins are a class of cholesterol lowering prescription medications and some early research indicates that they may reduce the risk of developing Alzheimer's. One can hypothesize that this finding is due to the beneficial effects on cholesterol levels and thus blood flow. This research is in its infancy and these medications have potentially serious side-effects—their use should be carefully discussed with your physician.

7 *Moderate* alcohol consumption may confer some protective effects. Moderate is generally described as one drink of alcohol per day for a woman and two for a man. Red wine and beer have been studied the most and *moderate* use appears to have protective effects for a number of conditions. Drinking in excess of the amounts described here has deleterious effects.

8 Lifestyle. As a reminder, maintaining a healthy lifestyle has been shown in a number of studies to confer protection.

References:

Evans, R.M., Emsley, C. L., Gao, S., Sahota, A., Hall, K.S., Farlow, M.R., & Hendrie, H. (2000). Serum cholesterol, APOE genotype, and the risk of Alzheimer's disease: a population-based study of African Americans. *Neurology, 54(1)*, 240-242.

Kivipelto, M., Helkala, E-L., Laakso, M.P., Hanninen, T., Hallikainen, M., Alhainen, K., Soininen, H., Tuomilehto, J., Nissinen, A. (2001). Midlife vascular risk factors and Alzheimer's disease in later life: longitudinal, population-based study. *BMJ, 322*, 1447-1451.

Myers, A.; Holmans, P.; Marshall, H.; Kwon, J.; Meyer, D.; Ramic, D.; Shears, S.; Booth, J.; DeVrieze, F.W.; Crook, R.; Hamshere, M.; Abraham, R.; Tunstall, N.; Rice, F.; Carty, S.; Lillystone, S.; Kehoe, P.; Rudrasingham, V.; Jones, L.; Lovestone, S.; Perez-Tur, J.; Williams, J.; Owen, M.J.; Hardy, J.; Goate, A.M. (2000). Susceptibility Locus for Alzheimer's Disease on Chromosome 10. *Science, 290(5500)*, 2304-2305.

Alzheimer's Disease: Current And Future Perspectives On Therapy

Serge Gauthier, md, FRCPC
Professor and Director,
Alzheimer's Disease Research Unit,
McGill Centre for Studies in Aging, Montreal, Canada

Introduction

There has been a renewed interest in the therapy of Alzheimer's disease (AD) since the discovery in the late 1970's of a reduction of cholinergic activity in the brain of patients with AD, leading to the 'cholinergic hypothesis' for symptomatic therapy. This chapter will summarize the evidence for efficacy and safety of cholinesterase inhibitors (CI) in AD, and will provide a description of etiology-based hypothesis currently under testing in humans, potentially leading to disease modification. A suggested reading list is appended.

The cholinergic hypothesis and related drugs for Alzheimer's disease

The symptomatic treatment of AD is currently based on the hypothesis that many of the cognitive, functional and behavioral symptoms derive from a reduction in brain acetylcholine activity secondary to the loss of cholinergic neurons in the Nucleus Basalis of Maynert and other nuclei projecting to the hippocampus and mesial temporal region. The class of cholinergic drugs that has been most effective so far for the symptomatic treatment of AD is the CI (Table 1).

Table 1

Cholinergic drugs based on their modes of action

* Precursor loading	ex. choline, lecithin
* Stimulation of transmitter release	ex. linopirdine
* Slowing of transmitter degradation (CI)	ex. tacrine, donepezil, rivastigmine, galantamine
* Selective muscarinic agonists	ex. xanomeline

Only the four CI (tacrine, donepezil, rivastigmine and galantamine) have shown adequate safety and efficacy for general prescription use for the symptomatic treatment of AD, and they are considered as 'standard therapy, although of small average degree of benefit', based on Class I evidence. The data from the published literature on these CI are derived from randomized clinical trials of three to twelve months duration, in mild to moderately severe stages of 'probable AD', operationally defined as 5 to 26 on the Mini Mental State Examination of Folstein (MMSE), corresponding to the stages 3 to 6 on the Global Deterioration Scale of Reisberg.

There are common characteristics among CI. In terms of efficacy, the measurable short term (6 months) improvement in cognition and global functioning is comparable between CI at therapeutic doses (Table 2). The benefit on activities of daily living (ADL) has been demonstrated for all CI and best described as a slowing of decline rather than an actual improvement of specific ADL. An improvement of some neuropsychiatric symptoms has been shown with all CI, the pattern observed being an improvement in apathy and hallucinations. The CI also may delay emergence of neuropsychiatric symptoms. Age, gender and apoE genotype do not seem to be determinant factors in response to therapy, nor is the disease stage within the mild to moderately severe range. In other words, all patients with AD in the mild to moderate stages have an equal chance to improve.

Table 2

Cholinesterase inhibitors currently in use

Names	herapeutic doses	Particular features
Tacrine (Cognex)	30 or 40mg four times a day	need to monitor liver enzymes
Donepezil (Aricept)	5 or 10mg once a day	better in morning to avoid sleep disturbances
Rivastigmine (Exelon)	3, 4.5 or 6mg twice a day	slow titration allows for better GI tolerance
Galantamine (Reminyl)	8 or 12mg twice a day	the newest drug!

In terms of safety, the most common side-effects are gastro-intestinal (nausea, vomiting, diarrhea, anorexia). They are dose-related and transient, avoidable to a great extent by a slower titration up to therapeutic doses. These side-effects may be a limiting factor for the use of CI in patients of small body weight. Cardiovascular side-effects (symptomatic bradycardia, syncope) are not frequent, if one is cautious in persons with sick sinus syndrome or other supraventricular conduction defects. Syncope can occur even in the absence of pre-existing cardiac history or electrocardiographic abnormalities.

Muscle cramps in the lower limbs can occur from cholinergic stimulation at the neuromuscular junction. These cramps are dose-related and usually transient.

Less common central side-effects are insomnia and exaggeration of depressive symptoms, which can be avoided by ingestion in the morning with donepezil, and treatment of depression prior to initiating CI therapy.

The following responses to CI can be observed in clinical practice: (1) obvious with return to hobbies and social activities, with or without improvement on Mini Mental State Examination scores; this 'awakening' may last six to twelve months, followed by a slower decline than anticipated for age of onset and severity of dementia at onset on therapy; (2) modest with a transient reduction in apathy and increase participation in conversation; (3) absent with clinical decline despite therapeutic doses, or failure to tolerate minimally effective doses.

If there is no clinically detectable improvement despite the maximal dose recommended or tolerated of a given CI, or if the patient has progressed to a severe stage of AD, the decision to withdraw treatment must be taken after discussion with the patient and his caregivers. In case of rapid deterioration off the drug, it is possible to restart the same or another CI. The other option is to switch to another CI. It is also possible for interested patients and caregivers to participate in a number of clinical trials with novel symptomatic or disease modifying drugs.

New treatment approaches for modifying disease progression

The first steps in attempts at modification of AD progression have been to understand its natural history, and develop outcomes appropriate to the stage of disease that is targeted for therapy.

The study of the natural history of AD has been facilitated by diagnostic research criteria. A number of longitudinal studies spanning from one to seven years have looked at annual changes in cognition and functional autonomy or at cumulative rates of nursing home placement and death. A number of clinical milestones have been described in AD (Table 3), some potentially useful as endpoint for clinical trials.

Table 3

Clinical milestones in Alzheimer's Disease

conversion from mild cognitive impairment to diagnosable AD
loss of selected instrumental ADL
emergence of neuropsychiatric symptoms
nursing home placement loss of self-care ADL

A novel design has been proposed by Petersen and consist of delaying the conversion from mild cognitive impairment (MCI; Table 4) to diagnosable AD over 3 years, with an expected rate of conversion of 15% per year in the placebo-treated group (Figure 1). There are currently a number of clinical studies looking at the potential preventive effects of COX-2 selective inhibitors, vitamin E, and CI such as donepezil, rivastigmine and galantamine, versus placebo. The validity of these studies may be enhanced by the addition of brain volumetric measurements on MRI scans, which would show a slower rate of atrophy for the whole brain or selected regions such as the mesial temporal lobe, in patients who are on active treatment versus those on placebo. The results of these studies will be available late 2003 and could have a major impact on how we approach the very early diagnostic stages of AD.

Table 4

Operational Definition of Mild Cognitive Impairment

subjective memory complaints
normal ADL
normal general cognitive performance
abnormal memory for age and education level
not demented clinically

Another way to assess the efficacy of new treatments in mild to moderate stages of AD is the add-on design (Figure 2), where a new drug or agent with potential disease-modification effects is added to a CI, the standard symptomatic treatment. There are a number of such agents now available, based on knowledge gained from basic research in transgenic mice, the study of human brains after biopsy or autopsy, and large-scale epidemiological population studies (Table 5).

Table 5

Treatment approaches testable for disease-modification

Agent or class of drug	Mode of action
Alzhemed	Prevention of aggregation of amyloid fragments
Gamma secretase inhibitors	Shift metabolism of amyloid precursor protein to nontoxic pathway
Immunotherapy ('vaccine')	Breakdown of amyloid plaques by antibodies
Neotrophin	Enhance activity of Nerve Growth Factor
Non steroidal anti-inflammatory drugs	Suppression of microglial and complement Activation
Statins	Induction of apoE or direct effect on amyloid Metabolism
Vitamin E	Antioxidant protection

The future of therapy for Alzheimer's disease

There is a genuine interest among primary care practitioners, neurologists, geriatricians and psychogeriatricians for an accurate diagnosis of AD, which is moving towards very early symptomatic stages. The global management of this condition includes the treatment of concomitant disorders such as depression, disease-specific drugs such as CI, and atypical neuroleptics when necessary. Since comprehensive support programs have been shown to increase the time spouse-caregivers are able to care for AD patients at home, a judicious combination of support programs from community and lay associations to pharmacotherapy is currently the best therapeutic approach in the mild to moderate stages of AD.

In the near future, clinical studies with MCI populations will have hopefully confirmed one or the other etiology-driven hypothesis, which will bring to the attention of clinicians a large number of persons with memory complaints. New diagnostic strategies will be needed to cope with these mildly symptomatic individuals. Those individuals estimated at risk of conversion from mild cognitive complaints to AD would be offered 'preventive' therapy.

At a population level, delaying onset of AD by 5 to 10 years would greatly reduce its prevalence within one generation, as predicted by Khatchaturian. Clinical studies of at least 5 years duration will be required to prove that an intervention will reduce the incidence of MCI or of AD in an aging population. If positive, these approaches will be promoted at the public health level. Already, it is appropriate to state that control of systolic hypertension will reduce the incidence of strokes, large and small, and thus reduce the incidence of dementia. It is hoped that in 5 to 10 years, primary care clinicians and specialists will be using an evidence-based approach to AD prevention, offering recommendations commensurate to the individual risk, as is currently done for the prevention of atherosclerotic cardio-vascular diseases.

Suggested readings

AMERICAN PSYCHIATRIC ASSOCIATION. (1994). Diagnosis and Statistical Manual of Mental Disorders (4th ed.). Washington, DC.

CUMMINGS, J.L., VINTERS, H.V., COLE, G.M. and KHACHATURIAN, Z.S. (1998) Alzheimer's disease. Etiologies, pathophysiology, cognitive reserve, and treatment opportunities. Neurology 51 (Suppl 1): S2-S17.

EMILIEN G., BEYREUTHER, K., MASTERS, C.L. and MALOTEAUX, J.M. (2000) Prospects for pharmacological intervention in Alzheimer's disease. Arch. Neurol. 57: 454-459.

FOLSTEIN, M.F., FOLSTEIN, S.E. and MCHUGH, P.R. (1975) Mini Mental State: a practical method for grading the cognitive state of patients for the clinician. J. Psychiat. Res. 12: 189-198.

GAUTHIER, S. (2002) Advances in the pharmacotherapy of Alzheimer's disease. CMAJ 166: 616-623.

KHACHATURIAN, Z. (1992) The five-five, ten-ten plan for Alzheimer's disease. Neurobiol. Aging 13: 197-198.

MCKAHNN, G., DRACHMAN, D., FOLSTEIN, M., KATZMAN, R., PRICE, D. and STADLAN, EM. (1984). Clinical diagnosis of Alzheimer's disease: report of the NINCDS-ADRDA workgroup. Neurology: 34, 939-944.

MITTELMAN, M.S., FERRIS, S.H., SHULMAN, E., STEINBERG, G. and LEVIN, B. (1996) A family intervention to delay nursing home placement of patients with Alzheimer's disease. J.A.M.A. 276: 1725-1731.

PETERSEN, R.C., SMITH, G.E., WARING S.C., IVNIK, R.J., TANGALOS, E.G. and KOHMEN, E. (1999) Mild cognitive impairment. Clinical characterization and outcome. Arch. Neurol. 56: 303-308.

ROSENBERG, R.N. (2000) The molecular and genetic basis of AD: the end of the beginning. Neurology 54: 2045-2054.

SCLAN, S.G. and REISBERG, B. (1992) Functional Assessment Staging (FAST) in Alzheimer's disease: reliability, validity, and ordinality. Int. Psychogeriatr. 4 (Suppl 1): 55-69.

Inquiries and reprint requests should be addressed to Dr Serge Gauthier, McGill Centre for Studies in Aging, 6825 LaSalle Blvd., Verdun, Québec, Canada H4H 1R3. serge.gauthier@mcgill.ca

Commonly Asked Questions

*My father was diagnosed with Alzheimer's disease. It seems
to be ripping my family apart. Is this common?*

Any major illness in the family can cause tremendous stress on
the family and the family system, and Alzheimer's is no exception.
Indeed, the nature of the disease may make it more stressful at
both individual and family levels than other types of diseases.

The strength of your family's bonds and psychological health
as a whole will be reflected in how the family copes after Alzheimer's
enters the family. We have previously discussed the different roles
family members may have taken on, or which may have been
unknowingly assigned by the family. Those roles can interfere with
effective coping after the diagnosis and during the sometimes long
period of time when caregiving becomes a family issue. And, as
previously discussed in this book, other family dynamics come
into play when major illness is diagnosed in a family member.

Among them are the role-reversals that become necessary when
adult children must care for their parents. We carry with us the
remnants of our childhoods, including the relationships with our
parents. When caring for an aging, ailing parent, old feelings and
grudges can surface to complicate the more straightforward
caregiving needs.

At this point in your life, your family has likely expanded to
include spouses and grandchildren. These positive developments
in the life-cycle of families can also lead to complications. There
are obvious practical issues, such as increased demands on time
that come with marriage and children. And you have also added
other dynamics to your family system—each spouse has his or her

own family history, and that family history will affect how he or she reacts to illness and caregiving.

If the person diagnosed with Alzheimer's has a living spouse, chances are that individual is elderly. When he or she insists on taking over all caregiving, problems may arise. Caregiving is exhausting and taxing for even young, healthy persons. When an elderly spouse, particularly one with his or her own health problems, insists on taking on all of the caregiving duties, tension may arise due to that individual taking on too much and risking his or her own well-being. Similarly, those who take on caregiving because other family members are not helping may begin to resent the lack of assistance, and the resentment will show itself in family relationships.

Modern Americans live busy lives, lives that are not typically centered around extended families. Alzheimer's requires family members to shift priorities and focus on both long-term and short-term family caregiving issues. Family members will differ in their abilities to cope with these changes, and these differences may cause tension. Old family dynamics may be temporarily shelved when a family crisis arises, but the dynamics will typically resurface, once the crisis period is over.

Read the sections in this book on dealing with family issues and assess your own situation as realistically as you can. Do what you can to make necessary changes at an individual level and at a family level. Realize that tensions will arise. Each family will hopefully do what he or she can to meet in the middle so that the whole family shares in caregiving and decision making have to be made. Realize that tensions will arise. Each family will hopefully differ in the degree to which they are able to be flexible. Each family member may come with his or her own individual burdens, which are sometimes the psychological ramifications of the relationships they had with your parents. Remember that your relationship with your parents may be very different than that of your sibling with your parents, and those differences are likely to be reflected in their individual approaches to the Alzheimer's and caregiving.

Be realistic but also kind to yourself. You can only change your approach to the situation. You can hold family meetings, you can share your concerns with family members, and you can encourage all to be open and honest about family issues. But ultimately you can't control those variables. The only person you can control is yourself and how you choose to handle situations as they arise.

How do I explain to my child that his grandfather has Alzheimer's?

The ability of children to understand Alzheimer's varies with age and maturity. When you explain any serious illness to a child, you must take the age of the child into account. His or her level of intellectual and emotional development will determine the extent to which any child can understand serious illness and death. Prior experiences can also help to determine a child's ability to understand. A child that has lost a pet or a loved one through death will likely have a greater understanding than a child of the same age who has never experienced illness and death. Children today are exposed to the media and may have some concept of illness and death, that have been gleaned from television and other sources. These concepts which may need to be addressed and corrected.

Infants obviously have no concept of what is happening in their environment, at least at an intellectual level. But they may sense changes in caregiving and in family members, so be aware that even infants can be affected by a serious illness in the family.

Toddlers aren't yet intellectually capable of understanding serious illness and the permanence of death. They do, however, sense changes in family members and your changed psychological status will be felt by your toddler. Toddlers can understand that Granny is "sick," but not the full ramifications of the illness.

Preschool-aged children typically do not understand that death is a permanent condition. They generally have learned about death through family discussions, the death of a pet or another grandparent, or through multimedia. But it is an understanding at a preschool level, and typically involves much magical thinking. Death has often been explained as someone going to heaven, and the child may accept that the loved one is in Heaven. But serious illness and death as an earthly condition generally is not yet understood. This type of thinking may include guilt over "causing" the illness or death in someone that they love. Children at this age often believe that they have done something, such as misbehaving, to cause illness or death. Preschool children are also likely to start asking questions about illness and death. It is important to answer questions in a straightforward, non-threatening manner. Answer only the question that has been asked and no more. This gives the child a chance to digest the information—if he or she has later questions and knows questions will be answered, the questions will be asked. And answering only the question that has been asked avoids overwhelming or frightening the child.

Elementary school aged children have a better, more realistic concept of illness and death. It still may be a mysterious process, and it may be frightening. Children at this age may show some fascination with the processes of illness and death. This is normal and healthy. Do not discourage the curious child. Again, answer questions in a straightforward manner and answer only those questions that are asked.

Most adolescents are fully capable of understanding all aspects of illness and death. Willingness to undertake caregiving roles will vary among adolescents just as that willingness varies among adults. Some teens may be reluctant to spend time or even visit with the individual with Alzheimer's disease. This is a difficult issue for many families. Take time to speak with the teens in your family if this is an issue and remember to respect their wishes just as you hope yours will be respected. For some teenagers, the prospect of seeing a beloved grandparent so infirmed is just too difficult to bear. Talk with your teens and, more importantly, listen. Grandchildren often have special emotional ties with their grandparents, and it's important to remember that teens may be experiencing different, but no less difficult, emotions than their parent are. Teenagers are also dealing with their own personal lives. It is important to allow their lives to continue on as normally as possible. Further shaping their identities, spending increased time with friends, and becoming increasingly independent from their families are crucial developmental processes that they should be encouraged to continue.

Children need to know that Alzheimer's is not something they can catch and that it is not something that happens to everyone when they get older. You can tell younger children that Alzheimer's is a disease that makes a person mixed-up and forgetful, but that their grandparent (parent, aunt, uncle) will always love them.

If the individual with Alzheimer's is prone to becoming agitated or aggressive, you must protect children. Younger children will not understand the aggression, and they'll become needlessly frightened of the individual with Alzheimer's. They are unable to separate and understand the difference between an aggressive "Granny" and the actions of a person with Alzheimer's, actions which are not under "Granny's" control. You do not want your child's memories of a beloved grandparent to be those of a person who was verbally or physically abusive. Do your utmost to protect children from that behavior. Often people with Alzheimer's disease who behave aggressively do so only during a circumspect phase of the disease, and the need to protect young children from that kind of behavior will be obviated when the behavior ceases.

Children often have a special ability to accept people for who they are. My children gave my Father hugs and kisses and cuddled up with him to watch cartoons. One of Dr. Lindsay's nieces had a special relationship with her grandfather throughout his Parkinson's disease, and when the two were together they were usually found with her perched on his lap, sometimes wheeling around with him in his wheelchair, and often firmly planting kisses on him when he least expected it.

Why does something like bath time turn into such an ordeal?

There are innumerable possibilities here. A small, cramped bathroom may make the person uneasy. The noise of the water running and the verbal cues you are using may be unnerving. The individual may have an irrational fear that he or she will go down the drain, as many young children fear. Your loved one may feel more vulnerable without clothing on. He or she may be embarrassed at having to have help with bath or showers, or with being naked in front of others. There can be many reasons why bath time can be difficult.

Try to explain each step in a soft voice. For example, say "I'm going to wipe your face. This will feel good." The softness of your voice will be comforting and the explanation will prevent startling the individual.

Start in non-threatening ways—start with a nice, gentle foot and hand bath, for example, rather than insisting jumping right into a full-fledged body wash. This approach sometimes helps to relax the individual and reassure him or her about safety and respect during this process. A therapeutic touch approach like the aforementioned may actually relax the individual. Allow the person to do as much independently as is possible.

Schedule in baths or showers at a time of day you know the person is generally calmer and more relaxed. Make sure that the bathroom is warm enough—the elderly and people with Alzheimer's may be more sensitive to cold than younger, healthier persons.

My mother is hiding things. Does this mean she doesn't trust us?

No. It is very common for people with dementia to hide, money, keys, false teeth, and almost anything that the individual deems valuable or important. And it is common to express a belief that people are stealing valuable items. Remember that this individual can no longer recall hiding the items, much less where they are. When one can't remember the last ten minutes, as well as one's relationship to the people in one's environment, a natural conclusion is that valuables have been stolen.

Your best bet is to remove valuables so that they can't be hidden in the first place. Leave the individual with a little money for that feeling of independence that money provides, and if you can replace items you have tucked away with others so that you aren't reinforcing the notion that items are being stolen. And do this with as few items as possible. In truth, some things will be hidden by the person with Alzheimer, and most of those items will eventually be found. In most cases, it is not the item itself that is important, but the individual's feeling that his or her belongings are missing is what counts.

If your loved one with Alzheimer's becomes distressed over missing objects, try to do what you can to relieve that distress. If it is money that is missing, remind the individual that he gave you the money to put in his bank account. Do so even if it's not the truth. Unfortunately, sometimes we have to lie under these circumstances. Do what you need to in order to put his concerns at rest. Miraculously produce five dollars and remind him that he gave it to you to hold. He does not need to know that you took the five dollars out of your own wallet, and that he never gave you anything to hold.

If your loved one is in a nursing facility or is among people who may not be completely trustworthy, remember that in institutional settings items *are* sometimes stolen. Sadly, the same may happen at home if there are many people going in and out of the home. You can't completely discount your loved one's report when he says that valuables have been stolen, but chances are likely that they have simply been hidden away and he doesn't remember doing so.

My wife can remember things that happened to her when she was a child but she doesn't remember our grandchild's name or the things we did last year. How can that be?

This is the nature of Alzheimer's disease. Memory storage and recall are complex processes in the brain. Put simply, the brain stores short-term memory and long-term memories to some extent in different parts of the brain. Memory is referred to as a unitary entity, but it is not. Just some of the components are immediate memory, short-term memory, long-term memory, remote memory, attention to information to be stored in memory, registration of that information in the brain, processing of the information to cause storage of information in memory, recall of information, and so on. One does not need to know all of the components, only that it an intricate and complicated conglomeration of different processes, all of which require intact brain structures.

To again oversimplify, in the case of long-term memory, one just has to recall memories stored in the brain for long periods of time. Compared to short-term memory, it is a relatively straightforward process. Short-term memory, on the other hand, requires both storage and recall. Storage itself is difficult—if you have ever studied for a test or tried to remember a set of driving directions you haven't written down, you know how difficult it can be for the intact brain. It is this storage process that becomes impaired relatively early in the disease. Eventually both storage and recall are affected and long-term memory becomes more impaired as the disease progresses.

For short-term recall when your loved one is still functioning fairly independently, provide cues for recall. For all of us, cues help with recall of information that we are having difficulty dredging up from memory. All of the women here who write about their parents note that their parents wrote notes for themselves to help with recall, including recalling the names of their own children and spouses. They provided themselves with cues for recall.

To help your loved ones stay connected as best they can, use photo albums or share with them your memories of things they did in the past. Relate to those things they can remember rather than dwelling on the things they cannot recall.

My mother was always a gentle person. She never even raised her voice at us. Now she goes into a rage over nothing. What is causing this change in her personality?

Your mother is having "catastrophic reactions." The disease is causing brain damage, and the damage makes it difficult for her to process and express emotions appropriately. She may overreact to something to which she previously would have had little or no emotional reaction. Rose similarly mentioned her father having catastrophic reactions even though he had always been a gentle man.

When this happens, speak gently to the person. Overreacting yourself will only make the situation worse. Try to distract her and engage her in an activity she enjoys. Do not try to restrain her unless it is necessary to protect her safety or that of people around her. Restraining her this will only cause her to panic and will make the situation escalate. Pay attention to the situations or events that cause these types of reactions, and try to avoid these in the future. At all times, whether these reactions are occurring or not, keep dangerous objects away from your loved one who has Alzheimer's disease—the danger or hurting herself or someone else is too great. Lock up items such as kitchen knives and limit access to only those persons who have to use them for meal preparation.

When this happens, do not argue with her. Arguing and disagreeing at this point will only exacerbate the reaction. Empathize with her frustration (or whatever emotion you interpret her having) and indicate that you understand. Reassure her. Don't ask her why she's behaving the way that she is—it is unlikely that she knows. And if she does know, it is unlikely that she'd be able to communicate it in a way that others would understand. In truth, many healthy adults don't know "why" they behave as they do much of the time.

Don't dismiss her emotions. Though the emotions may be expressed in ways that are surprising to you, the emotions themselves are real. People with Alzheimer's are vulnerable, and their world is confusing. They experience fears and anxieties that we don't always understand at the moment, but which is sometimes clearer if we later take the time to review situations.

And know at all times that this is the disease exerting its effect.

I understand that Alzheimer's disease is incurable. What will my loved one die of?

Alzheimer's disease is not curable. A person can live with the disease for up to twenty years, though more common is to live with it for about eight years after the onset of symptoms first noted by relatives (Larson, et al., 2004). The length of time people in general live with the disease is affected by other factors, including age at the time of diagnosis and overall health. The older someone is when Alzheimer's is diagnosed, the shorter the period of time he or she tends to live with the disease. If the individual has other health problems, these will obviously have an impact on health and longevity.

There are many different causes of death among people with Alzheimer's disease. Problems with swallowing can lead to inhaling (aspirating) food and liquids. This often leads to pneumonia (known as aspiration pneumonia). Increasing lack of activity can lead to blood clots, including pulmonary emboli (clots in the lungs). Infections of any kind can shorten the life of physically vulnerable individuals. For this and other reasons, skin care for bedridden individuals is critical—bedsores can easily develop, and those in turn can easily become infected. Problems with urination can also cause infections, as can the use of catheters. Falls, particularly those that lead to fractures, may lead to a rapid decline and death. Similarly, surgery and anesthesia are risky in a person with Alzheimer's—the anesthesia can cause cognitive decline and, for some people, can be fatal.

Other causes are events that the individual may have been vulnerable to even without the presence of Alzheimer's. Strokes, heart disease, and other serious health problems can all be the causes of death.

Often people with Alzheimer's stop eating near the end of their disease. Even during middle phases, getting someone with Alzheimer's to eat can be a problem. This particular issue can be eased by providing very small portions and providing a number of small meals per day. Many people with Alzheimer's won't respond well when faced with a plate heaped with food. Provide food on a solid colored plate, one that is colorful, to make visualizing the food easier. And, if necessary, help your loved one eat. Sometimes, just initiating the first movement with a spoon or placing the proper utensil in your loved one's hand will be sufficient to get eating started. But, eventually, all eating may stop. Your loved one and your family should have predetermined plans for this event so that you know what your loved one wants in terms of life-support. You may choose to provide hydration (liquids) via intravenous fluids but not to add artificial feeding. These are personal decisions and should be made long before your family member reaches this point.

We are in shock since learning of my mother's diagnosis. We want to keep her at home as long as possible, but we don't know where to begin to look for help. What do you suggest?

Just as you're doing here, educate yourself! Follow suggestions made in this book, and adapt them to fit your needs. The Alzheimer's Association also provides a wealth of information about caregiving. Contact the Social Services department of your local hospital. They may be able to provide you with a list of home health agencies, adult daycare centers, and other resources. There is a world of information available on the Internet. We've provided some web addresses in the back of the book—start with those reliable sites and do research! Hold a family meeting to determine who will undertake various caregiving tasks. Think creatively and flexibly to enlist help from various sources.

My family seems embarrassed by my father's illness. How can I help them open up to people and accept offers of assistance?

Sadly, there was a time in our history when people who behaved "differently" were hidden away. In America, we continue to work at ridding ourselves of that psychosocial history, though remnants of it can be seen in reactions like "embarrassment."

Remember that Alzheimer's is a medical illness over which none of us have control. Help your family to understand that your father is one among four-and-a-half million Americans suffering from the disease. You are far from alone. In fact, a Gallup poll conducted for the Alzheimer's Association in 1992 indicated that one in ten Americans had a relative with Alzheimer's disease and one in three Americans knew a person with Alzheimer's disease. If you're honest with people, they will understand and may even have experiences to share that could be helpful to you.

Asking for assistance is not weakness, though in our society that emphasizes independents, one sometimes feels "weak" when asking for assistance. To the contrary, we believe that a stubborn refusal to ask for or accept assistance when Alzheimer's involved is, itself, a weakness. Alzheimer's is a long, draining illness. It isn't one that the vast majority of people can take on single-handedly. Your strengths will be in knowing what kinds of assistance you need and learning to seek out—and accept—the assistance.

My mother keeps notes to remind herself of things. Recently I found a note with a list of our names on it. I can't believe she is forgetting our names. How could she have lost so much memory without us knowing it?

There can be many reasons for this. One is covering: embarrassment, fear, and so many other reactions to the problems people with Alzheimer's are beginning to develop, leads them to try to cover up the symptoms. Dad also kept lists of his family's names and their relationships to him and to each other. He finally stopped tucking the lists in his pockets or wallet and placed the lists on the refrigerator in plain sight.

It is natural for all of us to want to hold onto our independence and dignity for as long as possible. When you think about it, your mother is exhibiting a natural urge to remember the people who are important to her, and to preserve her dignity. People with early to early-moderate Alzheimer's disease learn to compensate, which is still possible for most people into moderate stages of Alzheimer's. The more cognitively able and flexible someone is prior to the onset of Alzheimer's, the easier it is for that person to later compensate for some deficits. Your mother's ability to compensate for forgetting something as familiar as her children's names is resilient and shows her ability to compensate for some of her deficits. This becomes increasingly difficult, and finally impossible, as the disease progresses. People will then, for example, write lists but soon forget that they have written them, and will eventually lose the ability to write or read the lists.

Sometimes, failing to notice the changes comes from misconceptions we have about the aging process. We often explain away cognitive slippages as a normal part of the aging process. In fact, the kinds of memory problems and other cognitive changes that occur even in early Alzheimer's disease are far outside the normal range for the over sixty-five age group.

Finally, family members may not see symptoms due to their own denial. Modern families are also increasingly busy and separated geographically. Sometimes our failures to recognize the early symptoms are a combination of the individual with Alzheimer's successfully compensating and covering up their symptoms, and this is added to our own psychosocial barriers to seeing and accepting that there may be a problem.

My husband and I have been happily married for thirty-eight years. He is constantly accusing me of having an affair. This started about three months after his diagnosis. No matter how much I try to reassure him that I have never been unfaithful, he refuses to believe me. Why is he doing this?

This is not uncommon. My parents are another example of this phenomenon—they were married for over fifty-five years and had never talked of divorce. One day, though, he went to a neighbor's house and announced that they were getting a divorce.

As the individual with Alzheimer's begins to forget recent events and to experience a lack of trust in the environment, it makes sense that something as precious as marriage would start to be included in paranoid fears. Your husband may be expressing his fears that you will leave him, he may be picking up on some of your stress, or he may simply be fabricating information in an attempt to make sense of his new reality. This claim is not unusual, and neither are claims that the individual with Alzheimer's is being unfaithful when that individual is in bed with his or her spouse. Under those circumstances, he may say something like, "You shouldn't be in here. If my wife sees you, we will be in trouble."

When your husband voices his belief that you are being unfaithful, gently reassure him that you love him and only him. And try to distract him by engaging in a pleasurable activity together. If you are both able, go for a walk. Holding hands during your walk may reassure him or is likely to distract him or lead him to forget this disturbing thought. Remember at all times that this is Alzheimer's speaking—don't take his accusations personally.

How can I ever be a hundred percent sure that my loved one had Alzheimer's disease or some other form of dementia?

Only through autopsy can a definitive diagnosis be made. If your family agrees to donate your love one's brain to a brain bank, this donation will help in the search to find a cure and you may be able to arrange for feedback about the accuracy of the diagnosis. But during your loved one's life with Alzheimer's, know that research has indicated that diagnoses are accurate in eighty-five to ninety percent of cases, so the likelihood that the diagnosis is accurate is good.

Why does my mother have temper flare-ups? Sometimes they come out of the blue!

Be sure to rule out any physical causes. Something that may cause discomfort in a healthy individual who can give voice to his or her discomfort may cause more severe discomfort in someone with Alzheimer's. And this is compounded because the individual can no longer tell you what the problem is. While we are loathe to compare adults to children, it can be useful to think about how an infant or toddler reacts when he or she is ill or afraid. Unable to put pain, discomfort or fear into words, it will tend to come out as behavioral problems.

If you have ruled physical causes, remember that your mother is continuing to experience emotions just as she did before. She will experience happiness, sadness, fear, and a host of other emotions. Try to understand why the outbursts may occur. What has happened just prior to the outburst? Look at the course of her day to ascertain what may have caused the outburst. What do you think she is trying to express? Look for patterns—do outbursts tend to occur more during specific times of the day? Perhaps your mother merely tires, and her outbursts reflect her fatigue.

Read the section in his book that deals with catastrophic reactions. The section will provide some hints that you'll find useful when it comes to understanding outbursts, as well as how to handle them when they occur.

Will my loved one continue to be seen by doctors if he is placed in a nursing home?

Facilities may differ regarding which physicians see your loved one, but all facilities are required to meet specific federal guidelines regarding physician care.

Your loved one must have his or her admission to the facility approved by a doctor. Federal law then requires any person admitted to a nursing facility to be seen once every thirty days for the first ninety days following admission. After that, federal law requires that your loved one be seen by a physician every sixty days for the duration of time spent living in the nursing facility. Following the initial visit by a physician, the law does allow for a physician's assistant, clinical nurse specialist, or nurse practitioner to make subsequent visits unless your loved one has a medical problem that can only be treated by a physician. Nursing homes must have 24-hour on-call emergency medical care.

In some facilities, your loved one can continue to be seen by his or her personal physician. Find out if that physician has medical privileges at the nursing facility and if that is something that the facility allows.

Are some nursing homes set up specifically for Alzheimer's patients? My father-in-law seems to need so much attention. Will they understand his needs?

While there are some nursing facilities that specialize in Alzheimer's, more commonly you'll find nursing facilities that have special sections for Alzheimer's patients. Special care units, as these are known, are becoming increasingly common because of the increased numbers and need of nursing home residents with dementia.

Too often, nursing homes may claim that they have special care units but the practice differs from the claims. Only twenty-three states have laws requiring nursing homes to disclose what specifically they provide on their special care units, as well as the fact that this type of care is often more expensive. If a nursing facility claims to have an Alzheimer's unit and specialized care, ask to tour the unit and speak with the personnel associated with the unit. Require that the nursing home specify the differences in care.

If a facility does not have a specialized unit, make sure that it is an appropriate and safe nursing home for your loved one. Will appropriate activities be provided? Is sufficient supervision available? Are there structures in place to prevent wandering? Ask about staff training and experience in treating persons with Alzheimer's disease. And talk to as many people in the community as you can—many will have first-hand knowledge about or experience with the facility.

Why do I feel so guilty? I have done everything that I know how to do to help make my father's quality of life as good as it can be. I still feel like I have let him down.

We often feel that we have failed people we love when they have serious illnesses. We feel helpless to "fix it" and make it go away. And we can only do so much to ease their lives at this point. The nature of Alzheimer's often leads family members to feel that they have failed their loved ones. We watch them move from being a mature, capable individual to being almost infant-like in the end. We want to protect them from the disease, to make it go away. And we can't. Our guilt is irrational, but that doesn't make it feel any less present. Remind yourself that you are doing everything humanly possible to help your father and make his life pleasant. To the extent that you can, let go of the guilt—it's a useless emotion at that point.

What other kinds of diseases can cause dementia such as the kind seen in Alzheimer's patients?

Other diseases that cause cognitive losses, some similar to Alzheimer's and some quite different in character and progression, include Parkinson's disease, Pick's disease, Lewy bodies disease, frontotemporal dementia, Jacob-Creutzfeldt disease, and vascular dementia. Dr. Lindsay indicated when discussing Alzheimer's disease that even treatable causes such as depression, vitamin B12 deficiency, and prescription medication interactions can cause symptoms that appear to the unpracticed eye to be very similar to dementia. It requires a professional evaluation to clarify the causes of cognitive decline.

There are excellent resources available on the Internet and at your local library that will better explain these various forms of dementia. We caution against self-diagnoses and second-guessing diagnoses, though. While physicians certainly aren't infallible, there are many traps to be found when one tries to make diagnoses based on information gleaned from books and the Internet. If you have doubts about the diagnosis, discuss them with the physician who made the diagnosis. If you suspect that your loved one may have another type of dementia, share your beliefs with that physician. Educating yourself about various kinds of dementias really becomes fruitless if you do it with the goal of finding any explanation other than Alzheimer's for your loved one's illness. Remember, many other dementias share features with Alzheimer's, and your loved one may have two illnesses (e.g., Alzheimer's and additive small strokes).

Hope

My Interview with Dr. Andre Delacourte

We wanted to end this book with the one thing that keeps us going: hope. If your loved one has already lost a lot of ground with Alzheimer's disease or another form of dementia, you have probably accepted that there is no cure at this time. But there is hope, which is found among the dedicated research scientists who have devoted their lives to finding treatments and a cure for Alzheimer's disease. Dr. Delacourte is one such researcher. His tireless dedication to understanding Alzheimer's and finding a cure has led to some of the significant advances in this field.

Dr. Delacourte was a pioneer in the biochemical characterization of PHF, a hallmark of Alzheimer's disease. He was the first to describe the concept of pathological tau proteins (1989), to describe the different biochemical signatures of tau proteins in Alzheimer's disease.

Dr. Delacourte is a staff scientist (Director of Research INSERM) in the INSERM Research Center in Lille, France. INSERM is the French Institute of Health and Medical Research.

Deborah was amazed to get an answer to her e-mail requesting more information about the current state of Alzheimer's research. She has found Dr. Delacoute to be a wonderful, warm, caring individual. He has not only continued to correspond with her, but he agreed to help me with this chapter. We decided that I would ask the question and he would do his best to answer them. Hopefully she has asked the questions that you too are wondering about. Admirably, Dr. Delacourte was able to respond in fluent English and the conversation is repeated verbatim.

Dr. Delacourte, how did you become interested in finding a cure for Alzheimer's disease?

Dr. Delacourte:

My boss told me to work on "microtubules" for my thesis. Microtubules are filaments found in all cells of the body. Since I was interested by the functioning of the brain and nerve cells, I worked on microtubules of nerve cells.

I realized (1975/1980) that microtubules are involved in numerous neurodegenerative disorders, and tried to work on microtubules from the human brain. I have been able to convince the head of the neurological department of Lille Hospital, Dr H. Petit, to work on a disease named Alzheimer's disease in U.S.A., and senile dementia of the Alzheimer type, and frequently senile dementia, in France. It took us several years to set up a strategy to collect brains, in perfect collaboration with families of patients. Later on, with these brain tissues, I have been able to demonstrate the concept of "pathological tau proteins" as a motor for Alzheimer's disease (1989.)

Now it is well admitted that Amyloid beta and Tau are the two motors of AD. (see Science issue of 24 August, page 1491).

When do you believe a cure will be found? Do you think it will be found during our lifetime?

Dr. Delacourte:

It will be like cancer. We will not switch from a non-cure to a cure, but we will win days, then months then years on AD. Remember that AD is extremely heterogeneous, like cancer.

We already are able to win years in certain circumstances. For example, if you check your blood pressure correctly, you delay the disease of several years. Anti-cholinesterases are already able to slow down the disease. Of course, we are waiting for a miracle, named "vaccination:, but nobody knows if it will work. But we will know that very soon.

Do you believe there is a strong link between heredity and Alzheimer's?

Dr. Delacourte:

There is frequently a link of our diseases with heredity, but as you put it, it can be strong or weak. It is strong in 0.3% of all AD cases and it is named familial AD. Of course you see how rare it is.

Otherwise, there are numerous weak links with the heredity and also environmental factors. You have genetic factors such as the apolipoprotein genotype, that are risk factors. You can have also factors that protect you. Environmental factors can prevent or accelerate your disease. It is said that two glasses of French red wine (Bordeaux) prevent (a little bit) the disease. There are scientific papers to demonstrate that. Frankly, I do not know if it is true, but these are good news for those that like to drink a good wine.

Are there things that a person can do to better increase their odds of not getting Alzheimer's disease?

Dr. Delacourte:

In fact, and unfortunately, there is no precise recipe for that, except the sound and basic rules to have a healthy body and a healthy brain. I am sure that a regular practice of your muscles and nerve cells helps.

Do you think there will be a test which can detect Alzheimer's disease rather than rule out all other causes for the symptoms?

Dr. Delacourte

There will be a test one day, based upon a combination of clinical data and biochemical analysis (analysis of the CSF or the blood). There is already a test for familial AD (extremely rare, hopefully) which is genetic.

The tests, like therapy, will improve progressively (specificity and sensitivity). Clinicians say that they are already able to give an early and reliable diagnosis. I am not sure.

How do research dollars become actual research funding? Can you give us an idea how money given to research affords scientists the backing for specific projects?

It is difficult to give you a precise answer. Complicated! Research is expensive, in general: salaries, products, sophisticated techniques. You could consider that the costs for products for a researcher is equivalent to his salary. Of course, it depends of the approach. There is likely huge differences between teams, and results are not always directly proportional to expenses.

Backing specific projects is a good way to boost research towards a precise problem or disease. But it is as difficult to find which precise project merits to be helped.

How important is it that people donate the brain of an Alzheimer's patient to a brain bank? What can be learned from this donation?

A few years ago, it was important to help AD research by giving to the researcher the possibility to work on AD brain tissue. Now, brain donation is more important to the family than to the researcher. Indeed, this is the only way to be sure that the patient was really affected by AD, since the definite diagnosis relies upon a neuropathological examination. To be 100% sure that the member of the family was affected or not by AD is giving a precious information, that could be used if there is a risk factor. Indeed, with the progress of Science, the new treatments to come are likely to erase the risk factor.

For research, in fact, it is now better to have systematic brain donation of patients that die in hospitals, or elsewhere, whatever the disease.

This is a way to study the first stages of brain diseases, and how the disease spreads in the brain. I have described the first stages of AD using brain tissues from non-demented patients

I know that you are working on a vaccine for Alzheimer's disease. Do you envision there someday being a vaccine which will be given preventatively as polio vaccine is given now?

Vaccination is a great (and US) discovery. If it works in its principle, it will not only slow down the disease, or stop it, but prevent it. It is said it is working on mice. Nobody knows if it is going to work on human beings.

A therapeutic trial will start, hopefully next month or November. We should know soon. So we do not have to envision a preventive treatment later. Either it is miraculous or not good at all. I do not forecast something in the middle.

Vaccination is based upon the principle that we have to get rid of amyloid deposits, that are toxic. Vaccination should be able to remove amyloid deposits. What if amyloid is not the neurotoxic? There is a strong ideology, or lobbying, to say it is. We will see. I hope it will work, but I have some doubts.

What words of hope would you give someone whose loved one has Alzheimer's disease, given that a cure is not available now.

I would try to find words that take into account the following points:

— *The best treatment of the first AD stages is likely given by the family, that has to give its love and an adequate care*
— *there are already drugs that slow down the disease*
— *vaccination is for to morrow and there is a hope*
— *the best treatment at the last stages of the disease is to place the patient in a specialized center.*

Epilogue

by Deborah Glover-Uetz

If life is about learning from your experiences, and I think it is, Dad's illness has taught me many things.

Alzheimer's disease has taught me to live each day as if it is my last . . . . with a memory. I have stopped waiting for tomorrow to enjoy things. When I think of Dad living in a world without thought, I appreciate the things I am able to think about and remember. The days are turning cool and fall is in the air. I can smell it. Dad didn't understand changes in season. I make sure to notice the crispness in the air and the changing colors in my world.

Alzheimer's disease has taught me that there are so many things that are matters of the heart and the world is full of people who need to share those emotions with someone else. Through the Internet my friends in the chat room came together and worked through our individual and shared experiences in a way that would have been impossible in another time. We learned lessons from each person who came along. We learned that you can go to someone you have never seen or heard the sound of their voice and share your deepest feelings. The chat room was our safe place where we could say anything without being judged. This same kind of safe place is waiting for you either on the Internet or in your local support groups. You too will find that you are going to learn from the other people and they will learn from you.

The time that Dad was ill was the hardest time of my life. Not were there the phone calls from the nursing home that began with "He is okay, but . . ." there were also the holidays, birthdays and family get-togethers that made us painfully aware of his absence. There were the dreams that he had passed away and the surprise when I awake to find he was still living. I suppose that was my subconscious preparing me for the inevitable. The lesson from this is, perhaps, don't take life for granted. Live it.

I have learned that there are research scientists who will take the time to answer questions which given their level of expertise must sound so simple. I learned that you will never get anything unless you ask. I have learned that sometimes it is the worst in people that rises to the surface when faced with a crisis. Sometimes it is the last person you would expect who steps up to the chaos and makes order of it. You will never know until tested if those you love will face the monster or turn and run.

Patience has been my Achilles' heel all of my life. I hate to wait for anything. I live life looking forward to a month from now. Throughout this ordeal the word "patience" has popped up more times than I can count. I had to wait for Dad's tests to tell us what was wrong. We waited to find a good placement for him. We in the chat room waited weeks to reconnect to one another when the system was down. The process of writing the book has been 10% writing and 90% waiting. Have I learned patience? No, but I am better at it than I was in the beginning.

I have learned that whether the common bond is Alzheimer's, cancer, depression, whatever . . . there are people out there who understand like no one else understands your pain. A shared experience is a powerful thing. There is no substitute for it.

I have empathy for those who are at the beginning of this experience, I feared for what lay ahead for Dad, and I had hope that research would find a cure. I still have that hope—it is too late for Dad, but it's not too late for others.

Just when I thought that this story had ended, as far as the book is concerned fate through something at the world that none of us could have imagined. On September 11, 2001, our world changed. We watched in terror and awe as passenger planes crashed into the World Trade Center, the Pentagon, and a field in Pennsylvania. Life would never be the same again.

Within moments I began to receive e-mails of concern from Rose in Australia, Dr. Delacourte in France, friends from the Mass.

General chat room in Canada, England, and all over the United States. Dr. Anne Lindsay, the daughter of the late John Lindsay, former mayor of New York City shared her sorrow over the plight of her former home city.

We who had spent so much of our past years grieving the loss of our loved ones health were now united in our concern and grief for our nation. Alzheimer's disease had brought us together but a lasting bond held us in place. Rose and I passed e-mails over the Internet checking on one another. From three continents we shared the concern for one another and for our families.

I don't know what lies ahead in the coming days, weeks, months and years but I do know that those who have spent time consulting with me on this book have become valued life time friends. God bless them all.

My brothers Keith and David shared their special gifts in helping care for Dad. David, an attorney was invaluable as Mom waded through legal questions and paper work. Dave's sense of humor buoyed Dad with each visit. Keith was like a diligent Shepard watching over his sheep. He kept track of every change in Dad's health from his home out of state and when he was able to visit his devotion to Dad inspiring. Our family had rowed the boat together and for that I am so grateful.

Table 1: Driving and Dementia

DRIVING AND DEMENTIA

The following is a reprinted with permission of the Hartford Financial Services Group. Their pamphlet addresses the issue of Alzheimer's, driving and dementia.

EARLY WARNING SIGNS OF DRIVING PROBLEMS INCLUDE:

- incorrect signaling
- Trouble navigating turns
- Moving into a wrong lane.
- Confusions at exits
- Parking inappropriately
- Hitting curbs
- Driving at inappropriate speeds
- Delayed responses to unexpected situations.
- Not anticipating dangerous situations
- Increased agitation or irritation when driving
- Scrapes or dents on car, garage or mailbox
- Getting lost in familiar places
- Near misses
- Ticketed moving violations or warnings
- Car accident
- Confusing brake for gas pedals
- Stopping in traffic for no apparent reason

Table 2: Coping with Problem Behaviors

The person may scream or yell inappropriately and may resist a caregiver's attempts to help with bathing, dressing or other personal care. Some physicians will prescribe anti-psychotic or calming medications.

Guidelines for Dealing With Behavior Problems

1   Everything surrounding a person could contribute to the behavior problem;

2   A thorough assessment of the elder, the environment and the caregiver by a trained professional is necessary in order to plan for intervention;

3   Think ahead and plan for situations that could result in problem behaviors;

4   Trying to argue or reason with a person who has Alzheimer's disease only results in frustration for both the caregiver and the elder. It is not possible to win an argument with a person who has Alzheimer's Disease;

5   Distract and divert whenever possible;

6   Keep the routine the same. Changes in routine are upsetting to people with Alzheimer's Disease and can cause behavior problems;

7   Promote a sense of security and comfort when problem behaviors occur. Problem behaviors often happen because a person is frightened and unable to make sense out of the environment;

8   Use positive reinforcement such as food, smiles, a gentle

touch, personal attention and lots of praise. These tools are more effective than negative reactions;

9   Allow a person with Alzheimer's disease some sense of control. Being able to save face is important even in a person who is very confused;

10   Maintain a calm manner when confronted with threatening behaviors. This can defuse a very tense situation and help a person become less fearful;

11   Keep things simple. Complex situations only cause frustration and can escalate behavior problems;

12   If a caregiver becomes frustrated and angry, it is best to find someone else to handle the problem and have the caregiver leave the immediate area or take a break (respite). An angry caregiver will only intensify problem behaviors;

13   Caregivers should practice ways to reduce stress when they become frustrated and angry. Deep breathing or talking to someone can be helpful. Remember that stress comes from many sources, including personal life;

14   Behavioral problems result from the disease. Don't take things that the person says and does personally. It is the disease speaking;

15   Be creative when seeking solutions to difficult behaviors;

16   Use good common sense when attempting to solve problem behaviors;

Keep a sense of humor even in the most difficult situations. Humor will help you cope with the frustrations of caring for a loved one with Alzheimer's disease.

Table 3: Communication Tips from The Ribbon Online

Closely related words are substituted for forgotten words. When you can't make out what a person with Alzheimer's Disease needs, point to the objects in question while asking questions like: "Do you want your purse? Your comb?" The person will have trouble understanding and following directions. Keep your sentences short and your directions clear. "Mother, fold the scarf." "Put the scarf in the drawer." "Close the drawer."

Tips and Techniques

1. Discuss important business during the morning when everyone is fresh;
2. Focus on one topic at a time;
3. Use specific words, names of people and objects;
4. Do not use pronouns or general language;
5. Words or events may be forgotten. Don't take it personally if birthdays or other special events are forgotten.

Toward the end, a person with Alzheimer's disease loses almost all ability to communicate or understand. Both long—and short-term memory are severely impaired, and he or she is totally dependent on the caregiver.

1. Continue speaking warmly, quietly and with eye contact;
2. Pat or stroke the person. Touch with love;

Smile. After all else is lost, a smile can calm and bring joy.

The Following Glossary Was Reprinted With Permission Of The Alzheimer's Association

A

abilities
Level at which certain actions and activities can be carried out.

acetylcholine
A neurotransmitter that appears to be involved in learning and memory. Acetylcholine is severely diminished in the brains of persons with Alzheimer's disease.

activities of daily living (ADLs)
Personal care activities necessary for everyday living, such as eating, bathing, grooming, dressing, and toileting. People with dementia may not be able to perform necessary functions without assistance. Professionals often assess a person's ADLs to determine what type of care is needed.

adult day services
Programs that provide participants with opportunities to interact with others, usually in a community center or facility. Staff leads various activities such as music programs and support groups. Transportation is often provided.

advance directives
Written documents, completed and signed when a person is legally competent, that explain a person's medical wishes in advance,

allowing someone else to make treatment decisions on his or her behalf later in the disease process.

adverse reaction
An unexpected effect of drug treatment that may range from trivial to serious or life-threatening, such as an allergic reaction.

age-matched controls
See controls.

agent
The individual—usually a trusted family member or friend—authorized by a power of attorney to make legal decisions for another individual. In scientific terms, "agent" sometimes refers to a drug as well.

aggression
Hitting, pushing, or threatening behavior that commonly occurs when a caregiver attempts to help an individual with Alzheimer's with daily activities, such as dressing. It is important to control such behavior because aggressive persons can cause injury to themselves and others.

agitation
Vocal or motor behavior (screaming, shouting, complaining, moaning, cursing, pacing, fidgeting, wandering, etc.) that is disruptive, unsafe, or interferes with the delivery of care in a particular environment. An abnormal behavior is considered agitation only if it poses risk or discomfort to the individual with Alzheimer's or his/her caregiver. Agitation can be a nonspecific symptom of one or more physical or psychological problems (e.g., headache, depression).

allele
One of two or more alternative forms of a gene; for example, one allele of the gene for eye color codes for blue eyes, while another allele codes for brown eyes.

Alzheimer's disease

A progressive, neurodegenerative disease characterized by loss of function and death of nerve cells in several areas of the brain, leading to loss of mental functions such as memory and learning. Alzheimer's disease is the most common cause of dementia.

ambulation

The ability to walk and move about freely.

amino acids

The basic building blocks of proteins. Genes contain the code fassembling protein of the 20 amino acids necessary for human growth and function.

amyloid

A protein deposit associated with tissue degeneration; amyloid is found in the brains of individuals with Alzheimer's.

amyloid plaque

Abnormal cluster of dead and dying nerve cells, other brain cells, and amyloid protein fragments. Amyloid plaques are one of the characteristic structural abnormalities found in the brains of individuals with Alzheimer's. Upon autopsy, the presence of amyloid plaques and neurofibrillary tangles is used to positively diagnose Alzheimer's.

amyloid precursor protein (APP)

A protein found in the brain, heart, kidneys, lungs, spleen, and intestines. The normal function of APP in the body is unknown. In Alzheimer's disease, APP is abnormally processed and converted to beta amyloid protein. Beta amyloid is the protein deposited in amyloid plaques.

animal models

Normal animals modified mechanically, genetically or chemically, used to demonstrate all or part of the characteristics of a disease. With models, researchers can study the mechanisms of a disease and test therapies.

antibodies
Specialized proteins produced by the cells of the immune system that counteract a specific foreign substance. The production of antibodies is the first line of defense in the body's immune response.

anti-inflammatory drugs
Drugs that reduce inflammation by modifying the body's immune response.

anxiety
A feeling of apprehension, fear, nervousness, or dread accompanied by restlessness or tension.

apathy
Lack of interest, concern, or emotion.

aphasia
Difficulty understanding the speech of others and/or expressing oneself verbally.

apolipoprotein E
A protein whose main function is to transport cholesterol. The gene for this protein is on chromosome 19 and is referred to as APOE. There are three forms of APOE: e2, e3, and e4. APOE-e4 is associated with about 60 percent of late-onset Alzheimer's cases and is considered a risk factor for the disease.

apoptosis
Programmed cell death.

APP
See amyloid precursor protein.

art therapy
A form of therapy that allows people with dementia opportunities to express their feelings creatively through art.

assay
The evaluation or testing of a substance for toxicity, impurities, or other variables.

assessment
An evaluation, usually performed by a physician, of a person's mental, emotional, and social capabilities.

assisted living facility
A residential care setting that combines housing, support services, and healthcare for people typically in the early or middle stages of Alzheimer's disease.

atrophy
Shrinking of size; often used to describe the loss of brain mass seen in Alzheimer's disease during autopsy.

autonomy
A person's ability to make independent choices.

autopsy
Examination of a body organ and tissue after death. Autopsy is often performed (upon request) to confirm a diagnosis of Alzheimer's disease.

axon
The arm of a nerve cell that normally transmits outgoing signals from one cell body to another. Each nerve cell has one axon, which can be relatively short in the brain but can be up to three feet long in other parts of the body.

B

behavioral symptoms
In Alzheimer's disease, symptoms that relate to action or emotion, such as wandering, depression, anxiety, hostility, and sleep disturbances.

beneficiary
An individual named in a will who is designated to receive all or part of an estate upon the death of a will maker.

beta amyloid protein
A specific type of amyloid normally found in humans and animals. In Alzheimer's disease, beta amyloid is abnormally processed by nerve cells and becomes deposited in amyloid plaques in the brains of persons with the disease.

Binswanger's disease
A type of dementia associated with stroke-related changes in the brain.

biomarker
Used to indicate or measure a biological process (for instance, levels of a specific protein in blood or spinal fluid, genetic mutations, or brain abnormalities observed in a PET scan or other imaging test). Detecting biomarkers specific to a disease can aid in the identification, diagnosis, and treatment of affected individuals and people who may be at risk but do not yet exhibit symptoms.

blood-brain barrier
The selective barrier that controls the entry of substances from the blood into the brain.

brain
One of the two components of the central nervous system, the brain is the center of thought and emotion. It is responsible for the coordination and control of bodily activities, and the interpretation of information from the senses (sight, hearing, smell, etc.).

C

calcium
An element taken in through the diet that is essential for a variety of bodily functions, such as neurotransmission, muscle contraction,

and proper heart function. Imbalances of calcium can lead to many health problems and can cause nerve cell death.

calcium channel blocker
A drug that blocks the entry of calcium into cells, thereby reducing activities that require calcium, such as neurotransmission. Calcium channel blockers are used primarily in the treatment of certain heart conditions but are being studied as potential treatments for Alzheimer's disease.

caregiver
The primary person in charge of caring for an individual with Alzheimer's disease, usually a family member or a designated healthcare professional.

care planning
A written action plan containing strategies for delivering care that address an individual's specific needs or problems.

case management
A term used to describe formal services planned by care professionals.

cell
The fundamental unit of all organisms; the smallest structural unit capable of independent functioning.

cell body
In nerve cells, the central portion from which axons and dendrites sprout. The cell body controls the life-sustaining functions of a nerve cell.

cell culture
Cells grown in a test tube or other laboratory device for experimental purposes.

cell membrane
The outer boundary of the cell. The cell membrane helps control what substances enter or exit the cell.

central nervous system (CNS)

One of the two major divisions of the nervous system. Composed of the brain and spinal cord, the CNS is the control network for the entire body.

cerebral cortex

The outer layer of the brain, consisting of nerve cells and the pathways that connect them. The cerebral cortex is the part of the brain in which thought processes take place. In Alzheimer's disease, nerve cells in the cerebral cortex degenerate and die.

cerebrospinal fluid (CSF)

The fluid that fills the areas surrounding the brain and spinal cord.

choline

A natural substance required by the body that is obtained from various foods, such as eggs; an essential component of acetylcholine.

choline acetyltransferase (CAT)

An enzyme that controls the production of acetylcholine; appears to be depleted in the brains of individuals with Alzheimer's disease.

cholinergic system

The system of nerve cells that uses acetylcholine as its neurotransmitter and is damaged in the brains of individuals with Alzheimer's.

cholinesterase

An enzyme that breaks down acetylcholine, into active parts that can be recycled.

chromosome

An H-shaped structure inside the cell nucleus made up of tightly coiled strands of genes. Each chromosome is numbered (in humans, 1-46). Genes on chromosome 1, 14, 19, and 21 are associated with Alzheimer's disease.

clinical trials
Organized studies that test the value of various treatments, such as drugs or surgery, in human beings.

coexisting illness
A medical condition that exists simultaneously with another, such as arthritis and dementia.

cognitive abilities
Mental abilities such as judgment, memory, learning, comprehension, and reasoning.

cognitive symptoms
In Alzheimer's disease, the symptoms that relate to loss of thought processes, such as learning, comprehension, memory, reasoning, and judgment.

combativeness
Incidents of aggression.

competence
A person's ability to make informed choices.

computed tomography (CT scan)
A type of imaging scan that shows the internal structure of a person's brain. In diagnosing dementia, CT scans can reveal tumors and small strokes in the brain.

conservator
In some states, the guardian who manages an individual's assets.

continuum of care
Care services available to assist individuals throughout the course of the disease.

controls
A group of people or animals that does not receive a treatment or other intervention or that is not affected with the disease being

studied. This group is used as a standard to compare any changes in a group that receives treatment or has the disease. In Alzheimer research patients are often compared with controls of the same age (age-matched) to rule out the effects of age on study results.

Creutzfeldt-Jakob disease
A rare disorder of infectious and genetic origin that typically causes memory failure and behavioral changes.

CT scan
See computed tomography.

cueing
The process of providing cues, prompts, hints, and other meaningful information, direction, or instruction to aid a person who is experiencing memory difficulties.

D

deficits
Physical and/or cognitive skills or abilities that a person has lost, has difficulty with, or can no longer perform due to his or her dementia.

delusion
A false idea typically originating from a misinterpretation but firmly believed and strongly maintained in spite of contradictory proof or evidence.

dementia
The loss of intellectual functions (such as thinking, remembering, and reasoning) of sufficient severity to interfere with a person's daily functioning. Dementia is not a disease itself but rather a group of symptoms that may accompany certain diseases or conditions. Symptoms may also include changes in personality, mood, and behavior. Dementia is irreversible when caused by disease

or injury but may be reversible when caused by drugs, alcohol, hormone or vitamin imbalances, or depression.

dementia-capable
Skilled in working with people with dementia and their caregivers, knowledgeable about the kinds of services that may help them, and aware of which agencies and individuals provide such services.

dementia-specific
Services that are provided specifically for people with dementia.

dendrites
Branched extensions of the nerve cell body that receive signals from other nerve cells. Each nerve cell usually has many dendrites.

diagnosis
The process by which a physician determines what disease a patient has by studying the patient's symptoms and medical history and analyzing any tests performed (blood, urine, brain scans, etc.).

disorientation
A cognitive disability in which the senses of time, direction, and recognition become difficult to distinguish.

DNA (deoxyribonucleic acid)
A chain of nucleotides (cytosine, guanine, adenine, or thymine) linked with ribose sugar molecules that form the basis of genetic material. Specific patterns of nucleotides represent particular genes.

double-blind, placebo-controlled study
A research procedure in which neither researchers nor patients know who is receiving the experimental substance or treatment and who is receiving a placebo.

Down syndrome
A syndrome that causes slowed growth, abnormal facial features, and mental retardation. Down syndrome is caused by an extra

copy of all or part of chromosome 21. Most individuals with Down syndrome develop Alzheimer's disease in adulthood.

durable power of attorney
A legal document that allows an individual (the principal) an opportunity to authorize an agent (usually a trusted family member or friend) to make legal decisions for when the person is no longer able to do so themselves.

durable power of attorney for healthcare
A legal document that allows an individual to appoint an agent to make all decisions regarding healthcare, including choices regarding healthcare providers, medical treatment, and, in the later stages of the disease, end-of-life decisions.

E

early-onset Alzheimer's disease
An unusual form of Alzheimer's in which individuals are diagnosed with Alzheimer's before the age of 65. Less than 10 percent of all Alzheimer patients have early-onset. Early-onset Alzheimer's is associated with mutations in genes located on chromosomes 1, 14, and 21.

early stage
The beginning stages of Alzheimer's disease when an individual experiences very mild to moderate cognitive impairments.

elder law attorney
An attorney who practices in the area of elder law, a specialized area of law focusing on issues that typically affect older adults.

electron microscope
A powerful microscope that employs a stream of electrons to magnify an image.

environment
Physical and interpersonal surroundings that can affect mood and behaviors in people with dementia.

enzyme
A protein produced by living organisms that promotes or otherwise influences chemical reactions.

estrogen
A hormone produced by the ovaries and testes. It stimulates the development of secondary sexual characteristics and induces menstruation in women. Estrogen is important for the maintenance of normal brain function and development of nerve cells. Estrogen is used therapeutically to treat breast and prostate cancer and osteoporosis, and to relieve the discomforts of menopause. Some research suggests that estrogen may be beneficial in preventing Alzheimer's disease. More studies are needed to confirm this.

excitotoxicity
Overstimulation of nerve cells by nerve impulses. Excitotoxicity often leads to cell damage or death.

executor
The individual named in a will who manages the estate of a deceased individual.

F

familial Alzheimer's disease
A form of Alzheimer's disease that runs in families.

fatty acids
Acids within the body derived from the breakdown of fats.

free radicals
Highly reactive molecules capable of causing damage in brain and other tissue. Free radicals are common by-products of normal chemical reactions occurring in cells. The body has several mechanisms to deactivate free radicals.

free-standing, dementia-specific care center
A facility solely dedicated to the care of people with dementia. This building can sometimes be part of a larger campus.

G

gait
A person's manner of walking. People in the later stages of Alzheimer's often have "reduced gait," meaning their ability to lift their feet as they walk has dimished.

gene
The basic unit of heredity; a section of DNA coding for a particular trait.

gene linkage
A group of genes located close together on a chromosome.

gene regulation
The control of the rate or manner in which a gene is expressed.

genetic susceptibility
The state of being more likely than the average person to develop a disease as a result of genetics.

genome
All the genes of an organism.

glucose
A simple sugar that is a major energy source for all cellular and bodily functions. Glucose is obtained through the breakdown, or metabolism, of food in the digestive system.

glutamate
An amino acid neurotransmitter normally involved in learning and memory. Under certain circumstances it can be an excitotoxin and appears to cause nerve cell death in a variety of neurodegenerative disorders.

guardian
An individual appointed by the courts who is authorized to make legal and financial decisions for another individual.

H

hallucination
A sensory experience in which a person can see, hear, smell, taste, or feel something that isn't there.

hippocampus
A part of the brain that is important for learning and memory.

hoarding
Collecting and putting things away in a guarded manner.

hospice
Philosophy and approach to providing comfort and care at life's end rather than heroic lifesaving measures.

Huntington's disease
An inherited, degenerative brain disease affecting the mind and body, characterized by intellectual decline and involuntary movement of limbs.

I

immune system
A system of cells that protect a person from bacteria, viruses, toxins, and other foreign substances that enter the body.

incontinence
Loss of bladder and/or bowel control.

inflammatory response
The immune system's normal response to tissue injury or abnormal stimulation caused by a physical, chemical, or biological substance. Immune system cells, if abnormally stimulated, can often cause further tissue damage while responding to the injured site.

instrumental activities of daily living (IADLs)
Secondary level of activities (different from ADLs, such as eating, dressing, and bathing) important to daily living, such as cooking, writing, and driving.

J

K

L

late-onset Alzheimer's disease
The most common form of Alzheimer's disease, usually occurring after age 65. Late-onset Alzheimer's strikes almost half of all people over the age of 85 and may or may not be hereditary.

late stage
Designation given when dementia symptoms have progressed to the extent that a person has little capacity for self-care.

layering
Behavior that involves inappropriately changing or layering clothing on top of one another.

Lewy body dementia
A dementing illness associated with protein deposits called Lewy bodies, found in the cortex of the brain.

living trust
A legal document that allows an individual (the grantor or trustor) to create a trust and appoint someone else as trustee (usually a trusted individual or bank) to carefully invest and manage his or her assets.

living will
A legal document that expresses an individual's decision on the use of artificial life support systems.

M

magnetic resonance imaging (MRI)
A brain scanning technique that generates cross-sectional images of a human brain by detecting small molecular changes. MRI scans reveal a contrast between normal and abnormal tissues. The image produced is similar to those generated by CT scans. There are no side effects or risks associated with MRI scans, although MRI can affect electrical devices like pacemakers and hearing aids.

Medicaid
A program sponsored by the federal government and administered by states that is intended to provide healthcare and health-related services to low-income individuals.

Medicare
A federal health insurance program for people age 65 and older and for individuals with disabilities.

memory
The ability to process information that requires attention, storage, and retrieval.

metabolism
The complex chemical and physical processes of living organisms that promote growth, sustain life, and enable all other bodily functions to take place.

microglia (microglial cells)
A type of immune cell found in the brain. Microglia are scavengers, engulfing dead cells and other debris. In Alzheimer's disease, microglia are found associated with dying nerve cells and amyloid plaques.

MID
See multi-infarct dementia.

Mini-Mental State Examination (MMSE)
A standard mental status exam routinely used to measure a person's basic cognitive skills, such as short-term memory, long-term memory, orientation, writing, and language.

mitochondria
Components found in cells that serve as primary energy sources for all cellular functions.

model system
A system used to study processes that take place in humans or other living organisms.

monoamine oxidase B (MAO-B)
An enzyme that breaks down certain neurotransmitters, including dopamine, serotonin, and noradrenaline.

monoamine oxidase inhibitor (MAOI)
A drug that interferes with the action of monoamine oxidase, slowing the breakdown of certain neurotransmitters. Used in the treatment of depression.

MRI
See magnetic resonance imaging.

multi-infarct dementia (MID)
A form of dementia, also known as vascular dementia, caused by a number of strokes in the brain. These strokes can affect some intellectual abilities, impair motor and walking skills, and cause

an individual to experience hallucinations, delusions, or depression. The onset of MID is usually abrupt and often progresses in a stepwise fashion. Individuals with MID are likely to have risk factors for strokes, such as high blood pressure, heart disease, or diabetes. MID cannot be treated; once the nerve cells die, they cannot be replaced. However, risk factors can be treated, which may help prevent further damage.

music therapy
Use of music to improve physical, psychological, cognitive, and social functioning.

N

nerve cell (neuron)
The basic working unit of the nervous system. The nerve cell is typically composed of a cell body containing the nucleus, several short branches (dendrites), and one long arm (the axon) with short branches along its length and at its end. Nerve cells send signals that control the actions of other cells in the body, such as other nerve cells and muscle cells.

nerve cell line
A group of nerve cells derived from a cell culture that can be used for experimental purposes.

nerve cell transplantation
An experimental procedure in which normal brain cells are implanted into diseased areas of the brain to replace dying or damaged cells.

nerve growth factor (NGF)
A protein that promotes nerve cell growth and may protect some types of nerve cells from damage.

neuritic plaque
See amyloid plaque.

neurodegenerative disease
A type of neurological disorder marked by the loss of nerve cells.
See Alzheimer's disease, Parkinson's disease.

neurofibrillary tangle
Accumulation of twisted protein fragments inside nerve cells.
Neurofibrillary tangles are one of the characteristic structural
abnormalities found in the brains of Alzheimer patients. Upon
autopsy, the presence of amyloid plaques and neurofibrillary tangles
is used to positively diagnose Alzheimer's.

neurological disorder
Disturbance in structure or function of the nervous system resulting
from developmental abnormality, disease, injury, or toxin.

neurologist
A physician who diagnoses and treats disorders of the nervous
system.

neuron
See nerve cell.

neuropathology
Changes in the brain produced by a disease.

neurotransmission
Passage of signals from one nerve cell to another via chemical
substances or electrical signals.

neurotransmitter
Specialized chemical messenger (e.g., acetylcholine, dopamine,
norepinephrine, serotonin) that sends a message from one nerve
cell to another. Most neurotransmitters play different roles
throughout the body, many of which are not yet known.

neurotrophic factor
A protein, such as nerve growth factor, that promotes nerve cell growth and survival.

nucleus
The central component of a cell; contains all genetic material.

O

onset
Defines time of life when Alzheimer's disease begins (e.g., early-onset, late-onset).

P

pacing
Aimless wandering, often triggered by an internal stimulus (e.g., pain, hunger, or boredom) or some distraction in the environment (e.g., noise, smell, temperature).

paranoia
Suspicion of others that is not based on fact.

Parkinson's disease
A progressive, neurodegenerative disease characterized by the death of nerve cells in a specific area of the brain; the cause of nerve cell death is unknown. Parkinson patients lack the neurotransmitter dopamine and have such symptoms as tremors, speech impediments, movement difficulties, and often dementia later in the course of the disease.

peripheral nervous system (PNS)
One of the two major divisions of the nervous system. Nerves in the PNS connect the central nervous system with sensory organs, other organs, muscles, blood vessels, and glands.

perseveration
Persistent repetition of an activity, word, phrase, or movement, such as tapping, wiping, and picking.

personal care
See activities of daily living.

PET scan
See positron emission tomography scan.

pharmacology
The study of drugs, including their composition, production, uses, and effects in the body.

phosphorylation
The chemical addition of a phosphate group (phosphate and oxygen) to a protein or another compound.

Pick's disease
Type of dementia in which degeneration of nerve cells causes dramatic alterations in personality and social behavior but typically does not affect memory until later in the disease.

pillaging
Taking things that belong to someone else. A person with dementia may think something belongs to her, even when it clearly does not.

placebo
An inactive material in the same form as an active drug,—for example, a sugar pill. See double-blind, placebo-controlled study.

plaques and tangles
See amyloid plaque and neurofibrillary tangle.

positron emission tomography scan (PET scan)
An imaging scan that measures the activity or functional level of the brain by measuring its use of glucose.

presenilins
Proteins that may be linked to early-onset Alzheimer's disease. Genes that code for presenilin 1 and presenilin 2 have been found on chromosomes 14 and 1, respectively, and are linked to early-onset familial Alzheimer's disease.

principal
The individual signing the power of attorney to authorize another individual to legally make decisions for him or her.

prions
Protein segments that may cause infection that may lead to some forms of dementia.

proteases
Enzymes that aid in the breakdown of proteins in the body.

protein metabolism
The breakdown of proteins into amino acids, a process essential to human growth and metabolism.

psychosis
A general term for a state of mind in which thinking becomes irrational and/or disturbed. It refers primarily to delusions, hallucinations, and other severe thought disturbances.

Q

quality care
Term used to describe care and services that allow recipients to attain and maintain their highest level of mental, physical, and psychological function, in a dignified and caring way.

R

reassurance
Encouragement intended to relieve tension, fear, and confusion that can result from dementing illnesses.

receptor
A site on a nerve cell that receives a specific neurotransmitter; the message receiver.

receptor agonist
A substance that mimics a specific neurotransmitter, is able to attach to that neurotransmitter's receptor, and thereby produces the same action that the neurotransmitter usually produces. Drugs are often designed as receptor agonists to treat a variety of diseases and disorders in which the original chemical substance is missing or depleted.

recombinant DNA technology
Artificial rearrangement of DNA; segments of DNA from one organism can be incorporated into the genetic makeup of another organism. Using these techniques, researchers can study the characteristics and actions of specific genes. Many modern genetic research methods are based on recombinant DNA technology.

reinforcement
Employment of praise, repetition, and stimulation of the senses to preserve a person's memory, capabilities, and level of self-assurance.

reminiscence
Life review activity aimed at surfacing and reviewing positive memories and experiences.

repetitive behaviors
Repeated questions, stories, and outbursts or specific activities done over and over again, common in people with dementia.

respite
A short break or time away.

respite care
Services that provide people with temporary relief from tasks associated with caregiving (e.g., in-home assistance, short nursing home stays, adult daycare).

restraints
Devices used to ensure safety by restricting and controlling a person's movement. Many facilities are "restraint free" or use alternative methods to help modify behavior.

risk factors
Factors that have been shown to increase one's odds of developing a disease. In Alzheimer's disease, the only established risk factors are age, family history, and genetics.

S

Safe Return
The Alzheimer's Association's nationwide identification, support, and registration program that assists in the safe return of individuals with Alzheimer's or related dementia who wander and become lost.

senile plaque
See amyloid plaque.

senility
Term meaning "old," once used to describe elderly diagnosed with dementia. Today, we know dementia is caused by various diseases (e.g., Alzheimer's) and is not a normal part of aging.

sequencing
In human behavior, doing things in a logical, predictable order.

shadowing
Following, mimicking, and interrupting behaviors that people with dementia may experience.

side effect
An undesired effect of a drug treatment that may range in severity from barely noticeable, to uncomfortable, to dangerous. Side effects are usually predictable.

skilled nursing care
Level of care that includes ongoing medical or nursing services.

special care unit
Designated area of a residential care facility or nursing home that cares specifically for the needs of people with Alzheimer's.

spinal cord
One of the two components of the central nervous system. The spinal cord is the main relay for signals between the brain and the rest of the body.

stages
Course of disease progression defined by levels or periods of severity: early, mild, moderate, moderately severe, severe.

sundowning
Unsettled behavior evident in the late afternoon or early evening.

support group
Facilitated gathering of caregivers, family, friends, or others affected by a disease or condition for the purpose of discussing issues related to the disease.

suspiciousness
A mistrust common in Alzheimer patients as their memory becomes progressively worse. A common example is when patients believe their glasses or other belongings have been stolen because they forgot where they left them.

synapse
The junction where a signal is transmitted from one nerve cell to another, usually by a neurotransmitter.

synaptic vesicles
Small sacs located at the ends of nerve cell axons that contain neurotransmitters. During activity the vesicles release their contents

at the synapse, and the neurotransmitter stimulates receptors on other cells.

T

tangles
See neurofibrillary tangles.

tau protein
The major protein that makes up neurofibrillary tangles found in degenerating nerve cells. Tau is normally involved in maintaining the internal structure of the nerve cell. In Alzheimer's disease, tau protein is abnormally processed.

tissue
A group of similar cells that act together in the performance of a particular function.

toxin
A substance that can cause illness, injury, or death. Toxins are produced by living organisms.

trigger
An environmental or personal stimulus that sets off particular and sometimes challenging behavior.

trustee
The individual or bank managing the assets of the living trust.

U

V

vesicle
A small pouch or pouch-like structure (sac). Vesicles in nerve cell axons contain neurotransmitters.

vitamins
Various substances found in plants and animals that are required for life-sustaining processes.

W

wandering
Common behavior that causes people with dementia to stray and become lost in familiar surroundings.

will
A legal document created by an individual that names an executor (the person who will managed the estate) and beneficiaries (persons who will receive the estate at the time of death).

X

Y

Z

zinc
A metal that is essential for proper nutrition. It is unknown if zinc plays a role in the development of Alzheimer's disease.

Updated 3/22/00

Work Sited

Elisabeth Kubler-Ross and David Kessler, Life Lessons—Two Experts on
   Death and Dying Teach Us About the Mysteries of Life and Living
Show Me the Way to Go Home, by Larry Rose
Diana Friel-McGlowin, Living in the Labyrinth
The Ribbon Online, An online newsletter for Alzheimer Care Giving
Dr. Andre Delecourte,
The Hartford Financial Group—Driving and Dementia
The Care Givers Stress Booklet
The Alzheimer's Association Glossary of Medical Terminology
The 36-Hour Day

A Family Guide to Caring for Persons with Alzheimer Disease,
Related Dementing Illnesses, and Memory Loss in Later Life. ISBN:
0-801861-49-7

The Alzheimer's Sourcebook for Caregivers: A Practical Guide for
Getting Through the Day ISBN: 0-737301-31-7

Alzheimer's Early Stages: First Steps in Caring and Treatment
ISBN: 0-897932-62-5

Alzheimer's Disease: Caregivers Speak Out

The Complete Guide to Alzheimer's-Proofing the Home

Facing Alzheimer's-Family Caregivers Speak

Handle With Care by Dorothy S. Brown

Printed in the United States
77116LV00002B/184